Mental Arithmetic 6

A

		Answer
1	154 + 67 =	
2	(2 × 45) + (1 × 45) =	
3	Write in digits the number one thousand one hundred and one.	
4	33% is larger than $\frac{1}{3}$. True or false?	
5	Write as a decimal $5 + \frac{5}{100}$.	
6	1.59 + 0.73 =	
7	1.5 × (1.5 + 2.5) =	
8	Approximate 7846 to the nearest thousand.	
9	a Calculate exactly, then b approximate to 1 decimal place. 8.64 ÷ 4	a b
10	If $a = 2$, find the value of $3a$.	
11	$4m = 10$ so $m =$	
12	$6^2 =$	

B

		Answer
1	86p + 35p + 71p =	£
2	Find 1% of £5.	p
3	Change 317mm to centimetres.	cm
4	510mm + 815mm = ... m ... mm = ... m	
5	90 days =	weeks days
6	An aeroplane flies 3900km in 6 hours. What is the mean (average) speed?	km/h
7	Find the perimeter of a rectangular field measuring 35m by 22m.	m
8	What size is the interior angle in each corner of an equilateral triangle?	°
9	Which letters of the word WAIST have at least one axis of symmetry?	
10	Approximate £13.63 to the nearest £1.	£

C

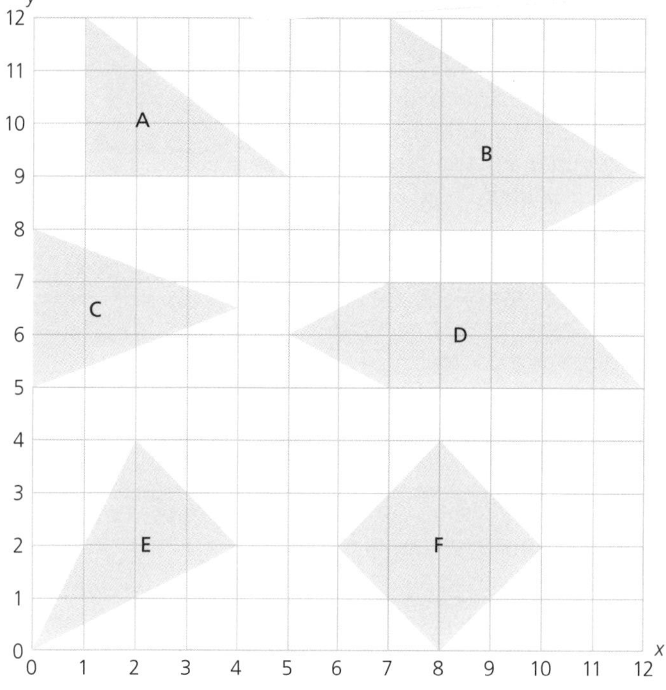

1 Write down the coordinates of each corner of triangle A. (,)

2 (,)

3 (,)

4 Write down the coordinates of the two corners of quadrilateral B that have the same x-value as each other. (,)

5 (,)

6 Write down the coordinates of the corner of triangle C that has the largest y-value. (,)

7 Write down the coordinates of the corner of pentagon D that has the smallest x-value. (,)

8 Write down the coordinates of the corner of triangle E whose x-value is twice the corresponding y-value. (,)

9 Write down the coordinates of the mid-point of the shortest side of triangle E. (,)

10 Write down the coordinates of the point where the diagonals of square F intersect each other. (,)

11 Estimate the coordinates of the mid-point of the longest side of triangle A. (,)

12 Estimate the coordinates of the mid-point of the longest side of quadrilateral B. (,)

A

		Answer
1	154 – 67 =	
2	(4 × 33) – 33 =	
3	Write in digits the number five hundred and five thousand five hundred.	
4	$\frac{3}{8} < 50\%$ True or false?	
5	Write as a decimal $\frac{5}{100} + \frac{8}{1000}$.	
6	2.07 – 0.09 =	
7	6.4 ÷ (2.5 – 0.9) =	
8	Approximate 8079 to the nearest hundred.	
9	a Calculate exactly, then b approximate to 1 decimal place. 15.165 ÷ 3	a b
10	If $x = 4$ and $y = 3$, find the value of xy.	
11	$5p = 10$ so p =	
12	15^2 =	

B

		Answer
1	£1.27 + 55p =	£
2	What is 6% of £40?	£
3	Change 455g to kilograms.	kg
4	850cm + 2.53m =	cm
	=	m
5	120 weeks =	years weeks
6	Write in kilometres per hour a speed of 18km in 10min.	km/h
7	Find the area of a footpath 0.8km long and 1.2m wide.	m^2
8	What size is the interior angle of each corner of a square?	°
9	Which letters of the word WAIST have more than one axis of symmetry?	
10	Approximate 1858mm to the nearest metre.	m

C

Answer

		Answer
1	Write down the coordinates of each corner of the trapezium E.	(,)(,)(,)(,)
2	Which shape has corner coordinates whose x-values are all positive and whose y-values are all positive?	
3	Which shape has corner coordinates whose x-values are all positive and whose y-values are all negative?	
4	Which shape has corner coordinates whose x-values are all negative and whose y-values are all positive?	
5	Which shape has corner coordinates whose x-values are all negative and whose y-values are all negative?	
6	Write down the coordinates of the corner of square D that has the most negative y-value.	(,)
7	Write down the coordinates of the corner of square D that has the most negative x-value.	(,)
8	Which shape has the same area as H?	
9	Which shape has half the area of B?	
10	Which shape has one side that passes through the origin?	
11	The coordinates of one corner of shape B have a y-value that is twice the corresponding x-value. Write down the coordinates of this corner.	(,)
12	The x-value and the y-value of the coordinates of two corners of shape H add up to zero. Write down the coordinates of these two corners.	(,)(,)

UPDATED FOR THE NEW NATIONAL CURRICULUM UPDATED

Schofield&Sims

Mental Arithmetic 6

Name

CONTENTS

NOTE FOR PUPILS AND TEACHERS

The organisation of the tests in this book differs from that in the earlier books:

- the Part A and B tests follow the same topic order from section to section, as shown below
- the Part C tests take the form of longer questions based on a problem-solving approach, allowing the topics introduced in Parts A and B to be developed in more depth.

Parts A, B and C

Each test appears on one page and is divided into three parts (see below). Parts A and B follow the same topic order throughout. Part C comprises longer problem-solving questions. Pupils may sit one test each week, with Parts A, B and C on separate days. Speed with accuracy is important, so a time limit of 10 minutes per part is recommended.

Part A **Questions 1–4: Number:** four operations with positive and negative integers (including remainders, brackets). Numbers in words and figures; powers/index notation. Fractions, decimals, percentages, ratios, mixed numbers. Equivalence; ordering (including negative numbers, symbols $<$, $>$).
Questions 5–9: Calculation: involving fractions, decimals, percentages and ratios. Four operations with decimals (including remainders, brackets). Approximations to significant figures/decimal places; estimations.
Questions 10–12: Algebra: substitutions, simple equations. Squares, square roots, cubes, factors, multiples, primes, sequences.

Part B **Questions 1–2: Money:** four operations, shopping, costing, sharing, ratio. Percentages, profit, loss; buying and selling; interest. Deposits, instalments; sales, discounts; foreign exchange.
Questions 3–6: Measurement: metric units, imperial units, conversions. Time. Compound measures.
Questions 7–9: Geometry: circumference, perimeter, area, volume of simple 2-D/3-D shapes. Angles of 2-D shapes including circles. Symmetry and order. Enlargements and scale factors.
Question 10: Approximations

Part C **Questions 1–12: Longer problem-solving questions:** coordinates: identification, location; reflections, translations, mappings. **Handling data:** graphs, tables, spreadsheets. **Scale drawings:** maps, charts. **Probability**. **Number puzzles:** number properties (revision); mathematical symbols. **Practical situations:** measures: length, area, money.

LANGUAGE OF MATHS

coordinates letters or numbers that are sometimes used on graphs or maps to help you find the exact position of something

decade a period of 10 years

decimal places the number of digits after the decimal point
Example write 6.92 to one decimal place (dp). You need to round the number so that there is only one digit after the decimal point, so 6.92 becomes 6.9

imperial measures before we used centimetres, metres, litres and kilograms (metric measures) everyone in Britain used imperial units for measuring
Example feet, yards, miles, pounds, stones, gallons

significant figures the number of digits needed to write a number that is accurate enough for a specified purpose

A

Answer

1 $154 \times 7 =$ ______

2 $(56 + 35) \div 7 =$ ______

3 Write in digits the number three-quarters of a million. ______

4 $17\% > 0.17$
True or false? ______

5 Write as a decimal $\frac{15}{100} + \frac{15}{1000}$. ______

6 $6.5 \times 20 =$ ______

7 $1.5 + (0.75 \times 4) =$ ______

8 Approximate 6.29 to the nearest tenth. ______

9 a Calculate exactly, then — a ______
b approximate to 1 decimal place. — b ______
$36.108 \div 6$

10 If $p = 3$ and $q = 8$,
find the value of $3p + 2 - q$. ______

11 $\frac{a}{5} = 15$ so $a =$ ______

12 $\sqrt{25} = 5$
Find the value of $\sqrt{64}$. ______

B

Answer

1 91p – 55p + 14p = £ ______

2 Find 0.5% of £7000. £ ______

3 Change 650ml to litres. ______ l

4 2148mm + 967mm = ______ m ______ mm
= ______ m

5 65 decades = ______ years

6 A car travels 27.4km in 20min.
Find its speed in kilometres per hour. ______ km/h

7 What size is the circumference of a circle of 80m diameter?

$\pi = 3.14$

______ m

8 At what angle do the diagonals of a square cross each other? ______ °

9 Which letters of the word MONEY have one, and only one, axis of symmetry? ______

10 There are 12 inches in a foot.
Approximate 88 inches to the nearest foot. ______ ft

C

Answer

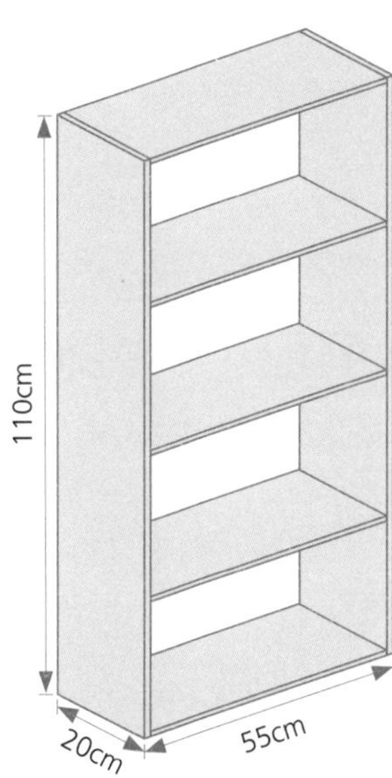

Nathan wants to make a bookcase for his bedroom.
It will be 110cm high and will contain four rows of books.
Each shelf will be 55cm long.

The planks of wood cost £3.00 per metre and can be bought in lengths of 250cm.

The planks are 20cm wide and 2cm thick.

1 What will it cost to buy each plank of wood? £ ______

2 How many planks will be needed for the two sides? ______

3 How many planks will be needed for the top, bottom and the shelves? ______

4 What is the total number of planks needed to make the bookcase? ______

5 How much will it cost to buy all the wood needed to make the bookcase? £ ______

6 How wide will the finished bookcase be, allowing for the thickness of the sides? ______ cm

7 What will be the total length of the shelves on which books can be placed? ______ cm

8 If the shelves are evenly spaced what is the size of the tallest book that will fit on the shelf? ______ cm

9 Nathan has a lot of books that are 25mm thick. How many of these books will fit on each shelf? ______

10 How many of these books will fit into the whole bookcase? ______

11 What is the total length of wood used to make the bookcase? ______ cm

12 Approximately what length of wood will Nathan have left over in total? ______ cm

SECTION 1 | Test 4

A

Answer

1 $154 \div 7 =$

2 $(11 \times 9) + (0 \times 9) =$

3 Write in words the number 60060.

4 Write the fraction $\frac{3}{20}$ as a percentage. %

5 Express 20% of 0.25 as a decimal.

6 $4.5 \div 6 =$

7 $10 - (6.3 \div 10) =$

8 Approximate 0.044 to the nearest hundredth.

9 a Calculate exactly, then a
b approximate to 1 decimal place. b
2.1×3.2

10 If $s = 6$ and $t = 5$, find the value of $3t - s$.

11 $\frac{4}{15} \times \frac{10}{12} =$

12 $\sqrt{144} =$

B

Answer

1 £13.26 – 115p = £

2 What is 9% of £50? £

3 Change 2.5m to centimetres. cm

4 2650m + 8145m = km m
= km

5 $3\frac{1}{2}$ centuries = years

6 Katy cycles $4\frac{1}{2}$ miles in 20min. Find her mean (average) speed in miles per hour. mph

7 Find the circumference of a coin of diameter 7cm to the nearest whole centimetre.

$\pi = 3.14$

cm

8 The smallest angle of a right-angled triangle is 30°. What sizes are the other angles? ° °

9 Which letters of the word VAPOUR have a vertical axis of symmetry?

10 Approximate 606g to the nearest kilogram. kg

C

Answer

The table below is part of a spreadsheet. The computer can perform calculations on the data held in each cell by applying a mathematical formula.

For example, the value in cell D2 is found by using the formula B2*C2 where * means multiply (i.e. £6.50 = £0.65 × 10).

The formula used to calculate the total cost of £47.02 is SUM(D2:D9). That is, £47.02 is found by adding together all the values in cells D2 to D9.

	A	B	C	D
1	Cakes ordered	Price each	Quantity	Cost
2	Doughnut	£0.65	10	£6.50
3	Cupcake	£1.99	6	£11.94
4	Fruit cake	£2.99	4	£11.96
5	Gingerbread man	£0.99	5	£4.95
6	Belgian waffle	£1.49	2	£2.98
7	Bakewell tart	£2.49	1	£2.49
8	Macaroon	£0.45	4	£1.80
9	Chocolate éclair	£0.55	8	£4.40
10	Total			£47.02

1 Write down the contents of cell A5.

2 Write down the contents of cell B9. £

3 Write down the contents of cell D4. £

4 Which cell contains the word 'Macaroon'?

5 Which cell contains the value 8?

6 Which cell contains the value £2.98?

7 What is the result of multiplying the contents of cell B8 by the contents of cell C8? £

8 Which cell of the table above contains the answer to Question 7?

9 What is the result of applying the formula B5*C5? £

10 What is the result of applying the formula SUM(C2:C9)?

11 Into which empty cell would you write the answer to Question 10?

12 Write down in words what the result of the formula in Question 10 tells you.

A — Answer

1. 1001 × 12 = ______
2. 154 ÷ 25 = ______ r ______
3. Add together two thousand and eight and eight thousand and two. Answer in digits. ______
4. Express 2% as a decimal. ______
5. Write $\frac{3}{5}$ of 7.5 as a decimal. ______
6. 21.3 – 7.8 + 8.7 = ______
7. 9.9 – (9.9 ÷ 9.9) = ______
8. Approximate 14.139 to two decimal places. ______
9. a Calculate exactly, then — a ______
   b approximate to 1 decimal place. — b ______
   0.05 × 3.22
10. $\frac{4}{8}$ ÷ 3 = ______
11. $a + 5 = 29$ so $a =$ ______
12. 2^3 = ______

B — Answer

1. 81p – £1.06 + 52p = ______ p
2. Increase £25 by 50%. £ ______
3. Change 1.1kg to grams. ______ g
4. 855g + 2.2kg = ______ kg ______ g
   = ______ kg
5. 4h 20min = ______ min
6. A car travels at a speed of 45km/h for 1h and then at 60km/h for 2h. Find the average speed of the car. ______ km/h
7. A 7.5cm line is enlarged by the scale factor 3. What is the length of the new line? ______ cm
8. The largest angle of an isosceles triangle is 100°. How big is each of the other angles? ______ °
9. Which letters of the word GROCER have a horizontal axis of symmetry? ______
10. 16oz equal 1lb (pound). Approximate 50oz to the nearest pound. ______ lb

C — Answer

The table compares monthly rainfall figures for Glasgow and London.

	Rainfall in millimetres	
Month	**Glasgow**	**London**
January	170	45
February	141	39
March	127	44
April	88	36
May	86	43
June	79	49
July	99	63
August	135	58
September	119	48
October	133	65
November	161	54
December	186	56
Annual total	1524	600

1. What is the total annual rainfall for Glasgow? ______ mm
2. What is the mean (average) monthly rainfall for Glasgow? ______ mm
3. In which month was the rainfall in Glasgow closest to the mean? ______
4. What fraction of Glasgow's annual rainfall fell in March? ______
5. What is the range of rainfall in Glasgow? (i.e. the difference between the wettest month and the driest month) ______ mm
6. By how much does the rainfall in Glasgow's driest month exceed that of London's wettest month? ______ mm
7. What is the total annual rainfall for London? ______ mm
8. What is the mean (average) monthly rainfall of London? ______ mm
9. In which month was the rainfall in London closest to the mean? ______
10. What percentage of London's annual rainfall fell in the driest month? ______ %
11. What is the range of rainfall in London? ______ mm
12. Which city, Glasgow or London, has the greatest range of rainfall? ______

A

Answer

1 $1001 \div 13 =$

2 $(50 \times 6) + (4 \times 50) =$

3 $(5 \times 10^3) + (2 \times 10^2) + (0 \times 10) + (5 \times 1) =$

4 Write 0.45 as a fraction in its lowest terms.

5 What number is 30% more than 1000?

6 $14.4 \div 1.2 =$

7 $8.8 - (8.8 \div 8.8) =$

8 Approximate 0.097 to two decimal places.

9 Work out correct to two decimal places. 5.271 + 1.527

10 $\frac{6}{15} \times \frac{5}{9} =$

11 $2t - 7 = 5$ so $t =$

12 $5^3 =$

B

Answer

1 21p × 5 = £

2 Reduce €120 by 10%. €

3 Change $\frac{1}{2}$l to millilitres. ml

4 6000kg + 3.5t = t kg

= t

5 36 hours = days

6 What speed in kilometres per hour is

a 6km in 3min a km/h

b 72km in 45min? b km/h

7 A notebook costs £1.00. An increase of 8p is added. What is the percentage increase? %

8 At what angle do the diagonals of a rhombus cross each other? °

9 Which letters of the word MUSIC remain the same after a rotation about the centre by 180°?

10 Decrease £15.00 by 2%. £

C

Answer

The diagram shows a plan of a two-bedroomed flat. The gridlines are spaced 1cm apart.

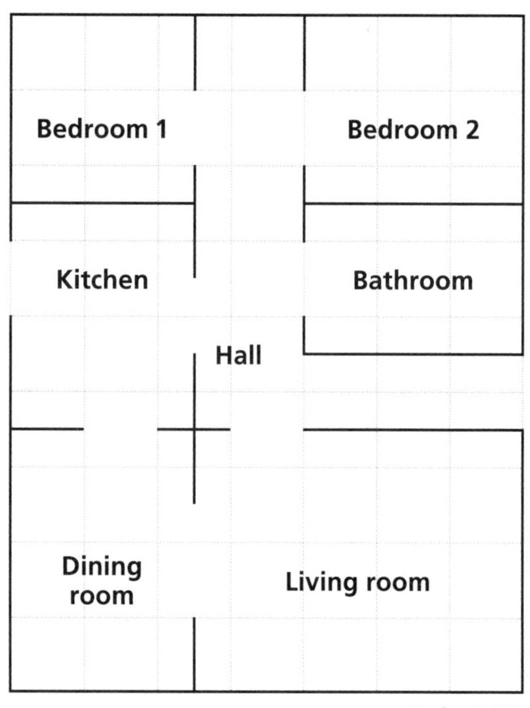

Scale: 1:100

1 What length is represented by 1cm on the plan? m

2 What size is bedroom 1? m by m

3 What is the area of bedroom 1? m^2

4 What size is bedroom 2? m by m

5 What is the area of bedroom 2? m^2

6 What is the cost of carpeting both bedrooms at £10 per square metre? £

7 What is the cost of carpeting the living room at £20 per square metre? £

8 How many tiles 250mm square will be needed to cover the kitchen floor?

9 How much will they cost if tiles are 80p each? £

10 The bath takes up 22% of the floor area of the bathroom. What is the area of the bath? m^2

11 Which has the bigger area, the hall or the dining room, and by how much? by m^2

12 What is the perimeter of the flat? m

A

Answer

1 $67 + 54 + 33 =$

2 $(540 \div 9) \div 9 =$ r

3 $(3 \times 10^4) + (2 \times 10^3) =$

4 Express 250% as a mixed number.

5 Add 20% of 35 to 18% of 200.

6 $1.27 - 5.03 + 4.85 =$

7 $(2.5 - 1.0) \times (2.5 + 1.0) =$

8 Approximate 7.0826 to three decimal places.

9 $100 - 20 \times 4 - 3 =$

10 If $l = 12$, $b = 5$, $h = 2$, find the value of lbh.

11 $\frac{w}{4} + \frac{1}{2} = 2$ so $w =$

12 List the factors of 24.

B

Answer

1 £3.06 × 6 = £

2 How much interest at 5% is given on £600? £

3 Change 3170mm to metres. m

4 660ml × 5 = l ml

= l

5 Write in 24-hour clock notation 25 minutes to 1 p.m.

6 How long will it take to walk 112 miles at a rate of 8 miles/day? days

7 A tank 1.2m tall has a base of area $0.6m^2$. Find its volume. m^3

8 What size is the interior angle of each corner of a regular pentagon? °

9 If the word DOZEN is turned upside down, which letters look the same?

10 Find in hectares the area of a field 200m long and 100m wide.

1 hectare (ha) = $10\,000m^2$

ha

C

Answer

Abdul keeps a record of the number of times different kinds of birds visit his garden. Over a period of two days Abdul observed a total of 60 birds. He drew a graph to show the results.

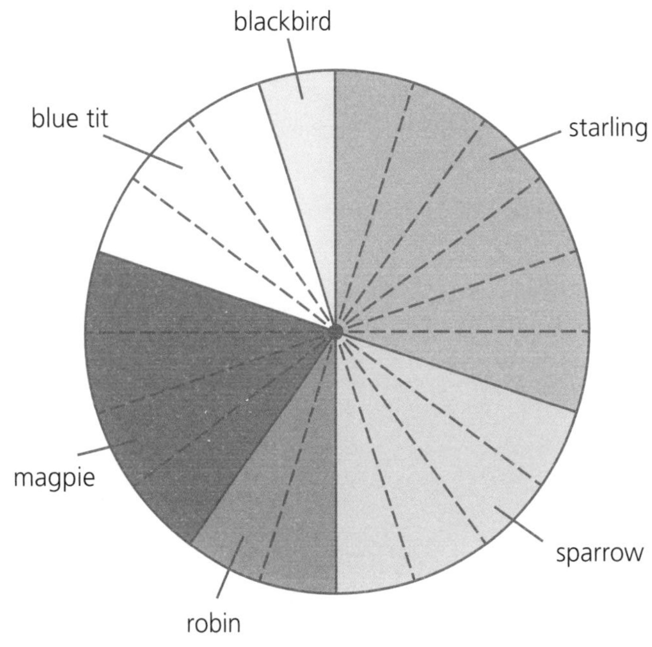

1 Which type of bird came to Abdul's garden most often?

2 Which type of bird was the least frequent visitor?

3 Which two birds visited in equal numbers?

4 What percentage of the total visits was made by robins? %

5 What percentage of the total visits was made by starlings? %

6 Five per cent of the total visits were made by which bird?

7 Which bird made 15% of the visits in the two-day period?

8 Which bird made 50% of the number of visits made by sparrows?

9 What was the number of magpies that came during the two days?

10 How many more sparrows than blue tits came to Abdul's garden?

11 How many times could Abdul expect to see a robin if he continued his observations for a full week?

12 Estimate the total number of birds that Abdul might expect to see in his garden in a week.

A — Answer

1 $67 + 54 - 21 =$

2 $540 \div (9 \div 9) =$

3 $2.5 \times 10^2 =$

4 Write 31.5% as a decimal.

5 Express $\frac{1}{2}$ of 24% as a decimal.

6 $0.2 \times 0.2 =$

7 $(3.6 \div 1.2) \times (3.6 + 1.2) =$

8 Approximate 623 to the nearest 10.

9 Work out correct to the nearest tenth. 0.72×2.7

10 If $a = 4$, find the value of $2a + 5$.

11 $2x + 22 = 30$ so $x =$

12 Write down the smallest number that will divide exactly by both 6 and 9.

B — Answer

1 £2.10 ÷ 5 = ______ p

2 A jacket costing £24 is reduced by 20%. How much do I pay? £ ______

3 Change 2055g to kilograms. ______ kg

4 1.435m × 6 = ______ m ______ mm

= ______ m

5 In which millennium was the year 1935? ______ millennium

6 How long will it take to drive 600km travelling at 80km/h? ______ h ______ min

7 Find the perimeter of a semicircle of diameter 10cm.

$\pi = 3.14$

______ cm

8 Find the area of a parallelogram with a base measuring 24.4cm and a height of 50cm. ______ cm^2

9 The word MERCHANT is painted on the outside of a glass door. Which letters look the same from the inside of the door?

10 Approximate 2888ml to the nearest litre. ______ l

C — Answer

The graph shows the number of rucksacks sold in one week by a sports shop. The average price of a rucksack sold by the shop is £8.50.

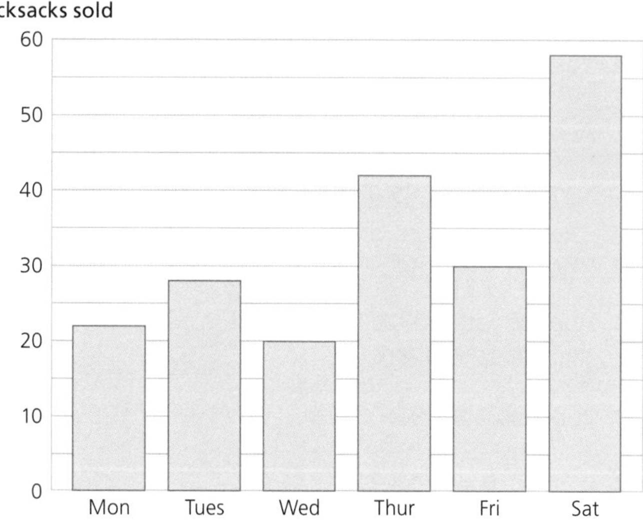

1 How many rucksacks were sold on Friday?

2 How much money did the shop take from rucksack sales on Friday? £ ______

3 Which day had the lowest number of sales?

4 What were the shop's takings from rucksacks on that day? £ ______

5 What was the largest number of rucksacks sold on one day?

6 On which day did sales increase the most as compared with sales on the day before?

7 What was the total number of rucksacks sold in the week?

8 How much money did the shop take from rucksacks in the week? £ ______

9 What was the mean (average) number of rucksacks sold each day during the week? Give your answer to the nearest whole one.

10 What percentage of the total weekly sales of rucksacks took place on Saturday? ______ %

11 On which day did the shop sell exactly 15% of the weekly total?

12 What percentage of the total weekly sales took place on the last three days of the week? ______ %

A

Answer

1 1760 – 880 = ______

2 85 ÷ 15 = ______ r ______

3 $\frac{4}{6} \times \frac{3}{10} =$ ______

4 Write the following in order of size, smallest first: $\frac{2}{3}$, 23%, 2.3 ______

5 What is 7.5% of 400? ______

6 0.5 × 0.6 = ______

7 1.05 + (2.4 × 1.5) = ______

8 Approximate 5270 to the nearest 100. ______

9 Work out correct to one decimal place. 5.271 + 1.527 ______

10 If $m = 7$, find the value of $2m + 5$. ______

11 $3x + 7 = 10$ so $x =$ ______

12 Write down the largest number that will divide exactly into both 24 and 32. ______

B

Answer

1 $6.50 ÷ 5 = $ ______

2 A t-shirt costing £8 is reduced by 15%. How much do I save? £ ______

3 Change 1470m to kilometres. ______ km

4 6.2m – 558cm = ______ cm
= ______ m

5 In which century was the year 1066? ______ century

6 A 6.5cm line is enlarged by the scale factor 4. What is the length of the new line in millimetres? ______ mm

7 Find the circumference of a wheel of radius 3cm.
π = 3.14 ______ cm

8 The smallest angle of a parallelogram is 50°. What size is the largest angle? ______ °

9 Which letters of the word CHALK have either a vertical axis of symmetry, or a horizontal axis of symmetry, but not both? ______

10 Approximate 188min to the nearest hour. ______ h

C

Answer

The Wilson family get a fares list and timetable to plan some trips.

Fares / Destination	Dep. code	Adult	Child	Return time
Nottingham	D	£4.95	£3.95	16:45
Skipton	B	£5.50	£4.80	18:00
Whitby	A	£5.85	£4.75	16:30
Haworth	C	£4.75	£3.85	16:30
York	E	£4.45	£3.95	16:00

Timetable	Departure code				
From	A	B	C	D	E
Barnsley	08:30	09:00	10:00	09:20	10:30
Dewsbury	08:50	09:50	10:50	08:30	10:50
Doncaster	–	08:30	09:30	09:50	–
Ossett	09:00	09:40	10:40	08:40	11:00
Wakefield	09:10	09:30	10:30	08:50	11:10

1 How much will it cost for Dad to take his two children to York? £ ______

2 At what time does the York coach depart from Barnsley? ______

3 Where does the York coach next pick up after leaving Dewsbury? ______

4 At what time is the last pick up point before going on to York? ______

5 If the coach takes 45 minutes to travel from Wakefield to York, at what time will it arrive at York? ______

6 At what time does the coach set off from York on its return? ______

7 How long do passengers have to visit York? ______ h ______ min

8 At what time does the Skipton coach leave Doncaster? ______

9 Where does the Skipton coach make its last pick up? ______

10 Where does the Nottingham coach begin its journey? ______

11 How long after leaving Doncaster does the Haworth coach make its last pick up? ______ h ______ min

12 Grandma gets a 50p reduction on the adult fare. How much will it cost for her and her grandson to go to Whitby? £ ______

A — Answer

1 $7006 - 6007 =$

2 $(85 \times 3) + (7 \times 85) =$

3 $1.7 \times 10^4 =$

4 Choose one from this list to fill the gap:
$1\frac{3}{4}$, 180%, $\frac{17}{10}$ — $1.7 <$ ______ $< \frac{45}{25}$

5 What is 7.5% of 4 as a decimal?

6 $3 \times (28 \div 2) =$

7 $\sqrt{64} + 5^2 =$

8 Approximate 3082 to the nearest 100.

9 Estimate to the nearest ten. 5.06×9.88

10 If $h = 13$, $k = 7$, find the value of $(h + k) \times (h - k)$.

11 $a + 5 = 0$ so $a =$

12 Which three of this set of numbers are prime? {1, 2, 5, 9, 15, 21, 23}

B — Answer

1 £15.05 ÷ 7 = £

2 A camera costing £85 is reduced by £17. What % saving is this? %

3 Change 3.542 tonnes to kilograms. kg

4 3.2t – 1455kg = ______ t ______ kg
= ______ t

5 If 14.11.2011 was a Thursday, what day was it on 22.11.2011?

6 An aeroplane travels 1km in 5sec. Find its speed in kilometres per hour. km/h

7 The circumference of a circle is 314mm. Find the diameter.
$\pi = 3.14$ mm

8 An isosceles triangle is drawn so that the largest angle equals the sum of the other two angles. How big is the largest angle? °

9 The word EXIT is painted on the inside of a glass door. Which letters look the same from the outside of the door?

10 Three TV programmes last 25min, 55min and 1h 35min respectively. What is the total of all three programmes to the nearest hour? h

C — Answer

Hamza owns a music shop. The supplier that Hamza uses to buy stock for his shop has increased its prices by 15%.

Musical instruments	Before 15% increase
Drum kit	£600.00
Piano	£1400.00
Electric guitar	£1000.00
Trumpet	£300.00
Violin	£200.00
Saxophone	£400.00
Accessories	
Speakers	£150.00
Channel mixer	£350.00
Plectrums (per ten)	£2.50
Sheet music	
Pupil book	£5.00
Sheet music album	£18.00

1 How much must be added to the cost of an electric guitar? £

2 What is the increase on a drum kit? £

3 What is the cost of a saxophone, including the 15% price increase? £

4 What will it cost Hamza to order three drum kits and two electric guitars, including the price increase? £

5 What is the cost of ordering 200 plectrums and 10 pupil books at the new increased price? £

6 What is the new cost of two speakers and a channel mixer? £

When Hamza sells his goods he adds a further 20% profit to the price he paid to the supplier.

7 What profit is added to the cost of a saxophone? £

8 What is the selling price of a saxophone, including profit? £

9 What profit does Hamza make by selling a violin? £

10 What is the selling price of a piano? £

11 What is the profit on an electric guitar with a speaker? £

12 What is the selling price of a sheet music album? £

A

		Answer
1	$1760 \times 11 =$	
2	$155 \div (15 - 5) =$	r
3	$2.05 \times 10^2 =$	
4	Write $\frac{49}{3}$ as a mixed number.	
5	Write $\frac{3}{20}$ of 5 as a decimal.	
6	Divide two-thirds by eight.	
7	$(6.3 \times 1.7) + (0.3 \times 6.3) =$	
8	Approximate 3.082 to one decimal place.	
9	Estimate to the nearest ten. 16.048×5.101	
10	If $p = 2.5$ and $q = 2$, find the value of $\frac{p}{q}$.	
11	$2x + 3x = 15$ so $x =$	
12	Write down the prime factors of 30 (i.e. those prime numbers which will divide exactly into 30).	

B

		Answer
1	£3.45 × 6 =	£
2	I buy a poster for £2.60 and sell it for £3.20. What is my profit?	p
3	Change $2\frac{1}{2}$km to metres.	m
4	2.5l – 955ml =	l ml
	=	l
5	If 23.06.2014 was a Monday, what date will it be on Thursday of the following week?	
6	A car travels 30km in 36min. Find its speed in kilometres per hour.	km/h
7	Find the circumference of a circle with radius 10cm. $\pi = 3.14$	cm
8	When full, the tank holds $10\,000\text{cm}^3$.	

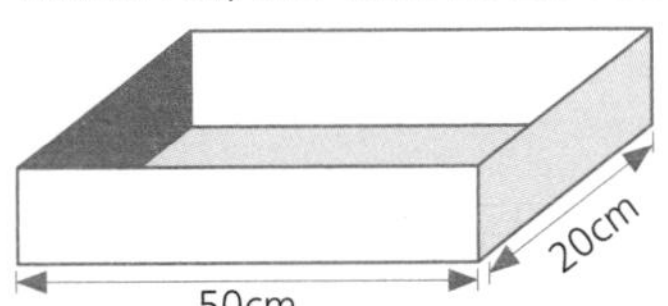

		Answer
	a Find its depth.	a cm
	b How many litres does it hold when full?	b l
9	Which letter of the word LAUGH has an axis of symmetry which is neither vertical nor horizontal?	
10	If two dozen pencils cost £1.95 find the cost of one pencil to the nearest penny.	p

C

Answer

Sairah and Jamie are playing a game with two dice and a coin. First they throw the dice and note down the numbers. Then they toss the coin. If the coin falls heads they add the two numbers from the dice. If the coin falls tails they multiply together the numbers from the dice. For example, throws of 3 and 2 on the dice will give a score of 3 + 2 = 5 if the coin falls heads and 3 × 2 = 6 if the coins falls tails. The first two lines of the table show more examples. Now fill in the blanks on the other lines.

	Throw 1	Throw 2	Heads	Tails
	2	5	7	10
	1	1	2	1
1	6	1	7	
2	4	2		8
3	3	6		
4	5		9	
5		6		12
6	6		12	
7		5		25
8	2			4
9			8	16

10	What is the largest score that can be made?	
11	What is the largest possible score if the coin falls heads?	
12	If they had another go and the score was 15, how did the coin fall, heads or tails?	

A — Answer

1. $1760 \div 16 =$
2. $(0 + 5) \times (5 - 5) =$
3. $3.17 \times 10^3 =$
4. Put the following in order of size, smallest first: $1\frac{1}{2}$, 0.5, 1.5%, $\frac{15}{50}$
5. Express 15% of 3 as a fraction in its simplest form.
6. $2 - 0.008 + 1.4 =$
7. $(2.2 \times 4.5) - (1.5 \times 2.2) =$
8. Approximate 1.057 to one decimal place.
9. Estimate to the nearest ten. $2480 \div 49$
10. $3y + 4 = 25$. Find the value of y.
11. Is 47 a composite or prime number?
12. Write down the next two numbers of the sequence. 1, 3, 7, 15, ▢, ▢

B — Answer

1. £100 ÷ 80 = £ ______
2. I put down a 10% deposit on a car costing £8750. How much is left to pay? £ ______
3. Change 3.3m to millimetres. ______ mm
4. 3.75m + 452cm + 1105mm = ______ m
5. The time 11:35 is the same as ______ minutes to ______
6. What is the length in millimetres when an 11.5cm line is enlarged by a scale factor of 3? ______ mm
7. Find the area of a square field whose perimeter is 60m. ______ m^2
8. A rhombus is drawn so that its smallest angle is half the size of its largest angle. What size is the smallest angle? ______ °
9. Which letters of the word BOUGHT have both a vertical and a horizontal axis of symmetry?
10. If 1000 envelopes cost £27, find the cost of one to the nearest 1p. ______ p

C — Answer

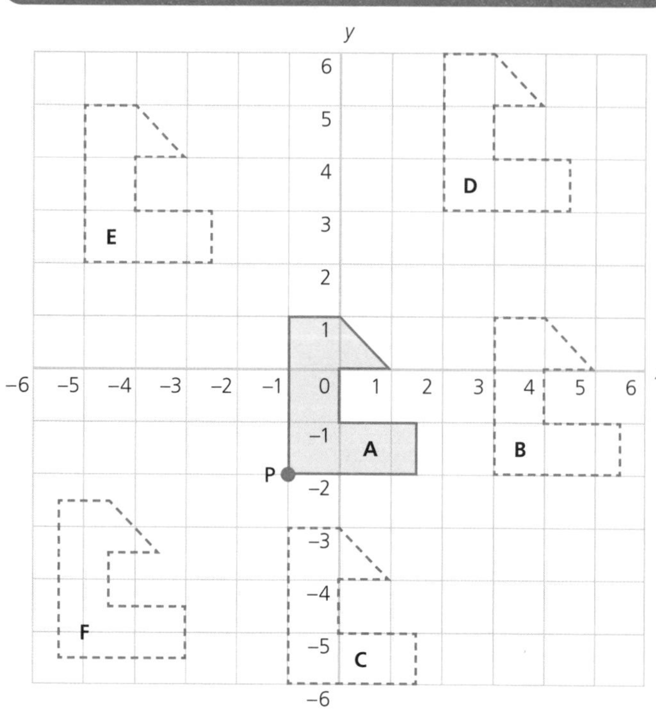

1. Write down the coordinates of point P on shape A. (____ , ____)
2. Write down the mapping which translates shape A to position B. $(x, y) \rightarrow (x +$ ____ $, y$ ____ $)$
3. Write down the mapping which translates shape A to position C. $(x, y) \rightarrow (x$ ____ $, y -$ ____ $)$
4. Write down the mapping which translates shape A to position D. $(x, y) \rightarrow (x$ ____ $, y$ ____ $)$
5. Write down the mapping which translates shape A to position E. $(x, y) \rightarrow (x$ ____ $, y$ ____ $)$
6. Write down the mapping which translates shape A to position F. $(x, y) \rightarrow (x$ ____ $, y$ ____ $)$
7. Write down the horizontal mapping that will bring point P to the y-axis. $(x, y) \rightarrow (x$ ____ $, y$ ____ $)$
8. Write down the vertical mapping that will bring point P to the x-axis. $(x, y) \rightarrow (x$ ____ $, y$ ____ $)$
9. Write down the mapping that will bring point P to the origin. $(x, y) \rightarrow (x$ ____ $, y$ ____ $)$
10. On the above grid draw in the position of shape A when translated by the mapping $(x, y) \rightarrow (x + 3.5, y - 3.5)$.
11. On the above grid draw in the position of shape A when translated by the mapping $(x, y) \rightarrow (x - 0.5, y + 4.5)$.
12. On the above grid draw in the position of shape A when translated by the mapping $(x, y) \rightarrow (x - 4.5, y + 0.5)$.

Name:		**Achievement Chart for Section 1** Tick the appropriate box for each question you got right.											
		1	2	3	4	5	6	7	8	9	10	11	12
Test 1	**Part A**												
	Part B												
	Part C												
Test 2	**Part A**												
	Part B												
	Part C												
Test 3	**Part A**												
	Part B												
	Part C												
Test 4	**Part A**												
	Part B												
	Part C												
Test 5	**Part A**												
	Part B												
	Part C												
Test 6	**Part A**												
	Part B												
	Part C												
Test 7	**Part A**												
	Part B												
	Part C												
Test 8	**Part A**												
	Part B												
	Part C												
Test 9	**Part A**												
	Part B												
	Part C												
Test 10	**Part A**												
	Part B												
	Part C												
Test 11	**Part A**												
	Part B												
	Part C												
Test 12	**Part A**												
	Part B												
	Part C												

REVISION TEST 1

1 $128 + 281 + 812 =$

2 $(156 - 65) \div 7 =$

3 $3.01 \times 10^2 =$

4 Express 350% as a mixed number.

5 Write 8% of 30 as a decimal.

6 $0.04 - 2 + 1.98 =$

7 $(3.2 - 2.3) \times (3.2 + 2.3) =$

8 Approximate 3.066 to one decimal place.

9 Calculate 2.995×4.037 correct to the nearest whole number.

10 If $a = 3$, $b = 4$, find the value of $a^2 + 2ab$.

11 $3p + 5 = p + 9$, so $p =$

12 $\sqrt{121} =$

13 €3.55 × 5 =

14 A pair of shoes costing £23.50 is reduced by 10% in a sale.
How much do I save?

15 Change 63.63cm to millimetres.

16 1.72kg + 5280g =

17 If 25 January is a Friday, what day will it be on 8 February?

18 A train goes at 72km/h for 20min. How far does it travel?

19 1cm on a map represents an actual distance of 800m.
Write the scale of the map.

20 The interior angle of each corner of a regular polygon is 90°.
How many sides does the polygon have?

21 Which letters of the words POST OFFICE have one,
and only one, axis of symmetry?

22 If a dozen exercise books cost £5.95, find the cost of
one book to the nearest 1p.

23 The coordinates of three of the corners of a square are
(0, 0), (0, 5), (5, 5). What are the coordinates of the other corner?

24 How many tiles 200mm square are needed to cover
a wall measuring 3m by 2.4m?

25 What is the length in centimetres when a 27mm
line is enlarged by a scale factor of 5?

REVISION TEST 1

Isla is helping her mother with their flower shop. They buy plants from the wholesaler and re-sell them in the shop. Isla uses a spreadsheet to look after their accounts.

	A	B	C	D	E	F	G	H	I
1	Name of	Buying	Number	Spending	Selling	Number	Income	Number	Value
2	plant	price	bought	on plants	price	sold	from plants	unsold	unsold
3	Buddleia	£2.71	15	£40.65	£3.25	44	£13.00	11	£35.75
4	Clematis	£3.75	12	£45.00	£4.50	6	£27.00	6	£27.00
5	Fuchsia	£0.79	65	£51.35	£0.95	33	£31.35	32	£30.00
6	Heather	£1.00	36	£36.00	£1.20	26	£31.20	10	£12.00
7	Hebe	£1.58	25	£39.50	£1.90	14	£26.60	11	£20.90
8	Hosta	£1.25	24	£30.00	£1.50	8	£12.00	16	£24.00
9	Lavender	£1.37	30	£41.10	£1.65	19	£31.35	11	£18.16
10	Potentilla	£2.37	12	£28.44	£2.85	7	£19.95	5	£14.25
11	Pyracantha	£2.08	10	£20.80	£2.50	8	£20.00	2	£5.00
12	Viburnum	£6.00	6	£36.00	£7.20	2	£14.40	4	£28.80
13			235	£368.84		127	£226.85	108	£216.25

26 What total number of plants do Isla and her mother buy?

27 What total amount do they spend in buying the plants?

28 What total number of plants do they sell on the stall?

29 What is their total income from selling plants?

30 What total number of plants is left unsold?

31 What is the total value of the unsold plants?

32 What is the most expensive plant they have for sale?

33 Which plant do they buy most of?

34 Which plant do they sell least of?

35 Which two plants bring in most income?

36 What is the buying price of a Heather plant?

37 What profit is made from selling each Heather plant?

38 What decimal fraction of the buying price is this profit?

39 What percentage profit is made from selling Viburnum?

The formula used to calculate the total number of plants bought is SUM(C3:C12).

40 What formula is used to find the total number of plants sold?

41 What formula is used to find the total income from plant sales?

The formula used to find the spending on Heather is B6*C6, where * means 'multiply'.

42 What formula is used to find the income from Heather plants?

43 What formula is used to find the income from Hosta plants?

The formula used to find the selling price of a Heather plant is B6 + (B6*0.2).

44 What formula is used to find the selling price of Viburnum?

45 What formula could be used to find the selling price of Clematis if they had wanted to make 25% profit?

A

Answer

1 Write the product of 15 and 25.

2 $(84 + 66) \div 30 =$

3 Write in digits 2.57 million.

4 Divide £45 in the ratio 2:7. :

5 Increase 20 by 20%.

6 $0.083 + 3.08 =$

7 $(1.25 \times 5) - (1.25 \div 5) =$

8 Approximate 1.603 to

a 2 decimal places a

b the nearest tenth. b

9 Estimate to the nearest ten.
28.6×3.22

10 If $x = 2$, $y = 3$, $z = 5$, evaluate $5x + 3y - 2z$.

11 $10x + 10 = 100$ so $x =$

12 What is the smallest number that is exactly divisible by both 6 and 8?

B

Answer

1 How many bags of crisps costing 40p each can I buy for £12?

2 A t-shirt at £10.50 is reduced by $33\frac{1}{3}$%. How much do I pay? £

3 1 foot = 12 inches. $28\frac{1}{2}$in = ft in

4 $3\frac{1}{2}$ft = in in

5 A TV programme lasts $1\frac{1}{4}$ hours. It begins at 6.50 p.m. At what time does it finish? p.m.

6 If 1l of water has a mass of 1kg, what is the volume in cm^3 of 1g of water? Note: 1l = $1000cm^3$ cm^3

7 Find the perimeter of a rectangular room 2.8m wide and 3.5m long. m

8 This triangle is enlarged by the scale factor 3. Find the perimeter of the new shape. cm

3cm
5cm
4cm

9 What is the number of axes of symmetry of a square?

10 Find 20% of £14.99 to the nearest £1. £

C

Answer

Luke and Iram share a set of six number cards. Each card has a single digit on it.

Luke's three cards are: 4 1 8

and Iram's cards are: 5 2 3

Help Luke and Iram to arrange their cards to answer the following questions.

1 What is the smallest three-digit number Luke can make?

2 What is the largest three-digit number Iram can make?

3 What is the largest three-digit even number Luke can make?

4 What is the smallest three-digit even number Iram can make?

5 What is the largest number exactly divisible by 5 that Iram can make?

6 Which two cards can Luke use to show a square number?

7 Which two cards can Iram use to show a power of two?

8 What is the largest prime number Iram can make with two of her cards?

9 What is the difference between Luke's largest three-digit number and Iram's smallest three-digit number?

10 What is the sum of Luke's smallest three-digit odd number and Iram's largest three-digit even number?

11 Luke makes the smallest two-digit odd number he can. He then multiplies this number by the digit remaining on his third card. What answer does he get?

12 Iram makes the largest two-digit even number she can. She then divides this number by the digit remaining on her third card. What remainder does she get? r

A — Answer

1. 500000 + 500 + 5 =
2. Write down
   a the quotient and — a
   b the remainder when 56 is divided by 9. — b
3. $2 \times 2 \times 2 \times 2 \times 2 = 2^x$. Find x.
4. Express 0.25 as a fraction in its simplest form and as a percentage. — a b
5. What is $\frac{2}{5}$ of 40?
6. $0.05 \times 45 =$
7. $\frac{2}{5} \div 12 =$
8. Approximate 112.345 to
   a 2 decimal places — a
   b the nearest ten. — b
9. Estimate to the nearest ten. $\frac{305 \times 21}{44}$
10. If $a = 3$, $b = 5$, evaluate $a^2 + b$.
11. $\frac{t+2}{5} = 4$ so $t =$
12. Express 30 as a product of prime numbers by filling in the blanks. — × × = 30

B — Answer

1. How many peaches costing 30p each can I buy for £10.50?
2. I buy a table for £120 with eight equal instalments. How much is each payment? — £
3. 3ft = 1yd. 7yd = ft — ft
4. 3yd = in — in
5. The 11:17 train to London arrives at 14:03. How long does the journey take? — h min
6. Find in millimetres the circumference of a circle with a radius of 50mm.
   $\pi = 3.14$ — mm
7. A glass sheet 6mm thick measures 110cm by 40cm. Find its volume in cm^3. — cm^3
8. A square with sides of 4cm is enlarged by the scale factor 2. What is the area of the new square? — cm^2
9. 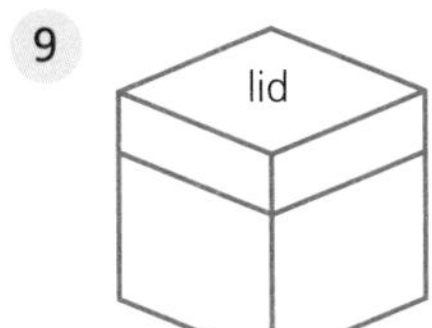

   A box has a square lid. In how many ways can the lid be turned so that it still fits the box?
10. Approximate 2940m to the nearest kilometre. — km

C — Answer

Harriet has five large photographs she wants to mount and frame. Each photograph measures 400mm by 300mm and is stuck onto a piece of mounting card measuring 500mm by 400mm. The mounting card and photo will then be placed under the glass in a wooden frame.

1. What is the size in metres of each piece of mounting card? — m by m
2. What is the area in m^2 of each piece of mounting card? — m^2
3. Each photo is stuck to the middle of the mounting card so as to give a border of equal width on all four sides. How many millimetres wide is this border? — mm
4. How many pieces of mounting card can be cut from a full sheet measuring 841mm by 594mm?
5. How many full sheets of card will Harriet need to buy in order to mount all five photos?
6. If a full sheet of card costs £2.35 how much will it cost Harriet to buy enough full sheets for all five photos? — £
7. Harriet orders some glass the same size as each piece of mounting card. What is the area in m^2 of each piece of glass? — m^2
8. If glass costs £11.20 per m^2 how much will each piece cost? — £
9. How much will it cost to buy the glass for all five photos? — £
10. What length of wooden beading will be needed to make each frame? Add on 10% extra from wastage. — m
11. The beading costs £3.15 per 2m length. How much will it cost to buy enough beading for all five frames? — £
12. What is the total cost for Harriet to frame all five photos? — £

A

Answer

1. $243 \div 27 =$
2. $24 - (15 - 3) =$
3. $11.01 \times 10^2 =$
4. Express $1\frac{1}{2}$ as a percentage. %
5. What is 150% of 3?
6. Write one-ninth as a decimal to 2 decimal places.
7. $(1.25 + 5) + (1.25 \times 5) =$
8. Approximate 69.802 to
   a 2 decimal places — a
   b the nearest whole number. — b
9. Estimate to the nearest 100. $6358 \div 7.8$
10. If $a = 3$, evaluate $5a^2$.
11. $5q - 40 = 0$ so $q =$
12. Express 28 as a product of prime numbers by filling in the blanks. $2 \times \_\_ \times \_\_ = 28$

B

Answer

1. If 10 bananas cost £2.40, then one will cost p
2. How long will it take to pay £27.50 at £2.50 per week? wk
3. 8 pints = 1 gallon. 40 pints = gallons
4. $2\frac{3}{4}$ gallons = ☐ pints pt
5. Pythagoras died in 497 BCE aged 85. In what year was he born? BCE
6. Find the cost of 2.25kg at 30p per $\frac{1}{2}$kg. £
7. A box is 5cm wide, 8cm long and 35cm high. Find its volume. cm^3
8. A square with an area of $25cm^2$ is enlarged by the scale factor 2. What is the area of the new square? cm^2
9. 

A cardboard square has its outline marked on a sheet of paper. What is the smallest angle of rotation of the square about its centre O that will bring it back onto its outline again? °
10. Approximate 20ft to the nearest yard. yd

C

Answer

The table below is part of a spreadsheet that Patrick used to calculate the squares and cubes of the numbers 1 to 10. Some of the values in the table are missing.

	A	B	C
1	Number	Square	Cube
2	1	1	1
3	2	4	8
4	3	9	
5	4	16	64
6		25	
7	6	36	216
8	7	49	343
9	8		512
10	9	81	729
11	10	100	1000
12	**Total**		**3025**

1. What is the content of cell B5?
2. What is the content of cell C11?
3. What is the content of cell A1?
4. What number is missing from cell A6?
5. What number is missing from cell C6?
6. What number is missing from cell C4?
7. What number is missing from cell B9?
8. The value of cell B7 was found by using the formula A7*A7.
   What formula was used to calculate the value of cell B10?
9. The value of cell C7 can be found by using the formula A7*A7*A7.
   What formula can be used to calculate the cube of 9?
10. What would be the result of using the formula A10*B10?
11. The value of cell C12 was found by using the formula SUM(C2:C11).
    What would be the result of using the formula SUM(B2:B11)?
12. What number is missing from cell B12?

A

Answer

1 $1000 - 587 + 113 =$

2 $24 \div (15 - 3) =$

3 Write in digits 10^6.

4 Write in order of size, starting with the smallest: 2:3, 2.3, 23%, $\frac{3}{2}$.

5 Divide 65 in the ratio 2:3. :

6 $0.6 \times 0.3 =$

7 $\frac{10}{12} \div 5 =$

8 Approximate 0.3572 to
a 2 decimal places a
b the nearest hundredth. b

9 Estimate $\frac{5964}{14.5 \times 4.1}$ to the nearest 100.

10 If $x = 3$, $b = 4$, evaluate $2x + y^2$.

11 $4a - 20 = 2a$ so $a =$

12 $6^3 =$

B

Answer

1 What is the change from £1 if I buy three tulips at 18p each? p

2 How many Euros for £50 at 1.2 Euros to £1? €

3 3ft 6in = in

4 15yd – 12ft = ft = yd

5 How many days inclusive from 14 March to 3 May? d

6 0.01 of 3.5l = ml ml

7 A wooden block measures 3cm × 4cm × 5cm. Find its total surface area. cm²

8 A right-angled triangle with sides of 3cm, 4cm and 5cm is enlarged by the scale factor 3. What is the length of the longest side of the new triangle? cm

9 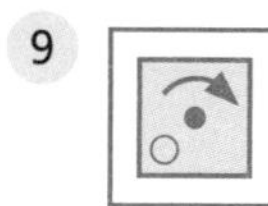 A cardboard square has its outline marked on a sheet of paper. How many times can the square be rotated 90° about its centre to bring it back onto its outline again?

10 Approximate 2444kg to the nearest tonne. t

C

Answer

The diagram shows a plot of land with a house and garden. The gridlines are spaced 1cm apart.

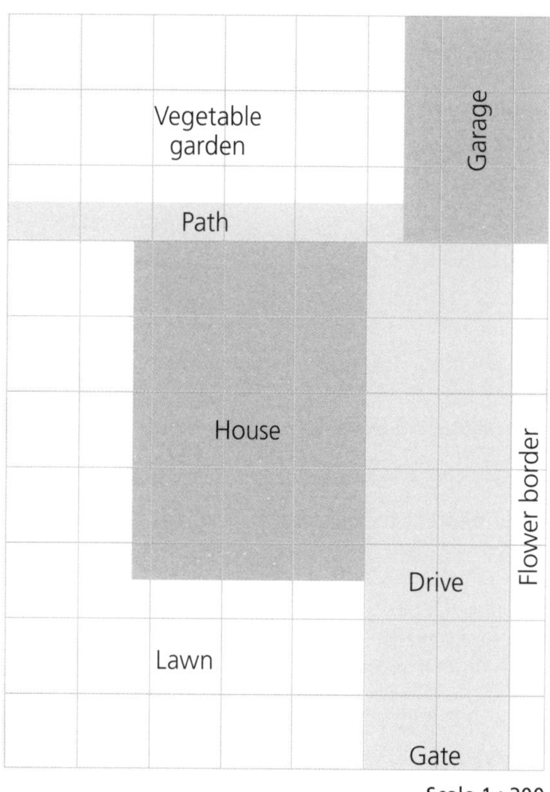

Scale 1 : 200

1 What length in metres is represented by 1cm on the plan? m

2 What size is the drive? m by m

3 What is the area of the drive? m²

4 Which has the bigger area, the drive or the vegetable garden, and by how much? by m²

5 What length of fencing is needed to go all round the plot, not including the gate? m

6 What is the total area of the plot? m²

7 What is the area of the garage? m²

8 What percentage of the plot is occupied by the garage? %

9 What is the area of the house? m²

10 What percentage of the plot is occupied by the house? %

11 What is the area of the lawn? m²

12 How many stone slabs 500mm square will be needed to pave the path?

SECTION 2 | Test 5

A

Answer

1 587 – 1000 + 643 =

2 24 ÷ (15 ÷ 3) = r

3 Write in digits 3.5×10^5.

4 Express $\frac{9}{25}$ as

a a decimal — a

b a percentage. — b %

5 Reduce 90 by 15%.

6 0.3 ÷ 0.6 =

7 $\frac{5 \times 4}{2}$ is how many times $\frac{0.5 \times 0.4}{0.2}$?

8 Approximate 0.0772 to

a 2 decimal places — a

b the nearest thousandth. — b

9 Calculate 52 ÷ 6 correct to two decimal places.

10 If $m = 6$, $n = 5$, evaluate $m^2 - n^2$.

11 $\frac{1}{2}(3 + x) = 4$ so $x =$

12 $\sqrt{49} =$

B

Answer

1 I buy magazines costing £1.35, £2.20 and 85p. How much change from £5? p

2 How many Euros for £500 at 1.25 Euros to £1? €

3 16oz = 1lb. 5lb 6oz = oz

4 3lb 12oz + 4lb 8oz = lb oz

5 How many hours and minutes between 8.46 a.m. and 3.22 p.m.? h min

6 $1m^3$ of olive oil has a mass of 920kg. What is the volume of 460g of oil? cm^3

7 A tank 0.75m tall has a square base with sides measuring 0.8m each. Find its volume. cm^3

8 A right-angled triangle with sides of 3cm, 4cm and 5cm is enlarged by the scale factor 3. What is the area of the new triangle? cm^2

9 What is the order of rotational symmetry of a square about its centre?

10 Approximate 165oz to the nearest pound. lb

C

Answer

The graph shows the land area of ten National Parks.

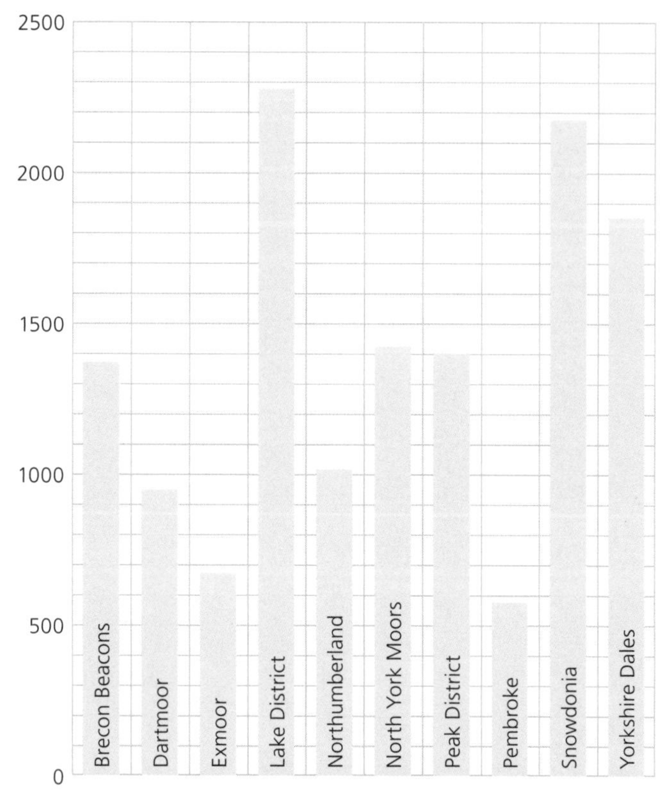

1 Which is the smallest National Park?

2 Which is the largest National Park?

3 Which park is approximately half the area of Northumberland?

4 The largest park is approximately how many times bigger than the smallest park?

5 Estimate the total area of all ten parks (to the nearest $100km^2$). km^2

6 Estimate the mean (average) area of the ten parks. km^2

7 Draw a line on the graph to show the mean area of the parks.

8 Which park is nearest in area to the mean?

9 The Brecon Beacons is approximately what percentage of the total area? %

10 Which park is approximately 5% of the total area?

11 Which park is approximately one-eighth of the total area?

12 The Lake District is approximately what fraction of the total area?

A — Answer

1 $221 \div 17 =$

2 $24 - (15 \times 3) =$

3 Write in digits 2^4.

4 The ratio of girls to boys is 7:3. If there are 28 girls how many boys are there?

5 Express $51 \div 8$ as a mixed number.

6 $5.02 - 0.502 =$

7 $2\left(\frac{3.6 + 4.8}{6}\right) =$

8 Approximate 0.008 22 to

a 2 decimal places — a

b 1 decimal place. — b

9 Estimate correct to the nearest whole number.
$(9.973 + 5.032) \div 2.986$

10 If $m = 6$, $n = 5$, evaluate $(m + n) \times (m - n)$.

11 $\frac{3}{p} = \frac{1}{3}$ so $p =$

12 Write the next two terms of the sequence.
1, 3, 6, 10, ▢, ▢

B — Answer

1 How much change from £10 if I spend £2.45, £1.80 and £3.75? £

2 What must I sell a £60 table for to make a profit of 30%? £

3 $2\frac{1}{2}$ gallons = pints

4 5lb 2oz – 3lb 10oz = lb oz

5 How many hours and minutes from 7.30 p.m. Friday to 11.15 a.m. Monday? h min

6 A park is approximately 300m square. What is its approximate area in hectares? ha

7 A wooden cube has a volume of $125cm^3$. How long is the cube's edge? cm

8 A line was enlarged by the scale factor 4. The new line is 72mm long. How long in centimetres was the original line? cm

9 ▭ What is the number of axes of symmetry of a rectangle?

10 Approximate $2\frac{1}{4}$ million square metres to the nearest square kilometre. km^2

C — Answer

Joe and Sidrah are baking cakes. Some of their recipes give quantities in cups and some in grams. They measure out five cups of flour and find that it weighs 800g. They plot a graph to convert from cups to grams.

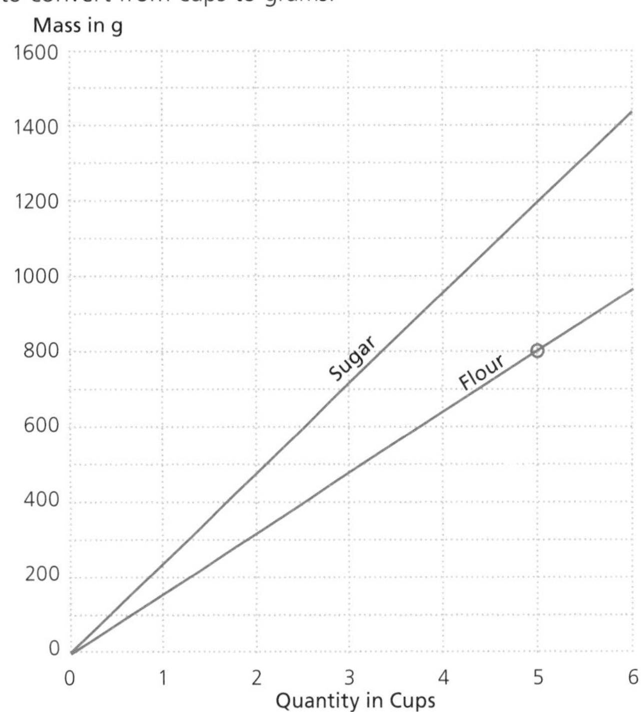

Use the graph to answer the following questions.

1 What is the mass of one cup of flour? g

2 What is the mass of $2\frac{1}{2}$ cups of flour? g

3 About how many cups of flour weigh 0.5kg?

Joe and Sidrah plot a conversion graph for sugar.

4 What is the mass of five cups of sugar? g

5 About how many cups are needed for 1kg of sugar?

6 Estimate the total mass of one cup of sugar and two cups of flour. g

7 How many times heavier is sugar than flour? (Hint: compare the mass of one cup of sugar with one cup of flour.)

Joe and Sidrah find that four cups of coconut weigh 380g and two cups of currants weigh 400g.

8 Plot these two points on the graph above.

9 Draw the conversion graphs for coconut and for currants.

10 About how many cups of currants weigh the same as five cups of flour?

11 About how many cups are needed for $\frac{1}{2}$kg of coconut?

A cake recipe needs three cups of flour, one cup of sugar and $1\frac{1}{2}$ cups of currants.

12 Estimate the mass of all these ingredients. kg

A — Answer

1 Write down the quotient when 105 is divided by 7.

2 $(80 \times 5) - (80 \div 5) =$

3 $20\,000 = 2 \times 10\,000$
$= 2 \times 10^x$ $x =$

4 Insert one of the symbols <, >, = to make this statement correct. 36% ____ $\frac{3}{8}$

5 $1\frac{1}{2} + \frac{5}{8} =$

6 $1.5 - 2.3 =$

7 $3.6 - (1.8 - 0.6) =$

8 Approximate 79 256 to the nearest hundred.

9 Give the answer to (0.07×0.08) correct to three decimal places.

10 If $x = 4$, $y = 2$, $z = 0$, evaluate $\frac{xy + z}{y}$.

11 $2 + a = 0$ so $a =$

12 Write the next two terms of the sequence.
2, 3, 5, 7, 11, ▢, ▢

B — Answer

1 If eight lollipops cost £1.76 then one will cost ____ p

2 I get 60% discount off my insurance premium of £240. How much do I pay? £

3 66ft = ____ yd

4 $1\frac{1}{2}$ gallons + 10 pints = ____ gal ____ pt

5 George can swim a length in 19.36s. Harry takes $\frac{3}{10}$s longer. What is Harry's time? ____ s

6 A pen was bought for £2 and sold at a profit of 45%. Find the selling price. £

7 Find in hectares the area of a rectangle 340m long and 100m wide. ____ ha

8 A line was enlarged by the scale factor 3. The new line is 5.4cm long. How long in millimetres was the original line? ____ mm

9 [lid] A box has a rectangular lid. In how many ways can the lid be turned so that it fits the box?

10 A box measures 1.9m long by 1.05m wide and is 0.55m deep. Find its approximate volume to the nearest cubic metre. ____ m^3

C — Answer

The graphs show annual weather data for Moscow. The bars represent the total monthly rainfall in mm. The line shows the maximum monthly temperature in °C.

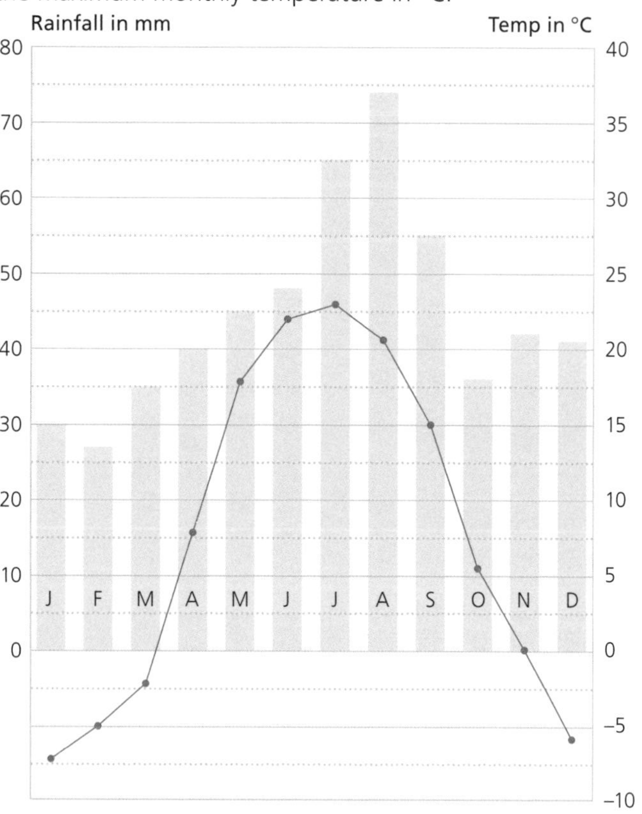

1 Which is the wettest month in Moscow?

2 Which is Moscow's driest month?

3 Which is the hottest month in Moscow?

4 Which is Moscow's coldest month?

5 During which five months is the maximum temperature at or below 0°C?

6 Which season (winter, spring, summer or autumn) is the driest?

7 Which season of the year is the wettest?

8 What is the total rainfall for the wettest three-month period? ____ mm

9 What is the mean (average) rainfall for these three months? (answer to the nearest mm) ____ mm

10 What is the mean (average) temperature over the hottest three-month period? (answer to nearest 1°C) ____ °C

11 What is the mean (average) temperature over the first four months of the year? (answer to the nearest 0.5°C) ____ °C

12 What is the mean (average) temperature over the five wettest months of the year? (answer to nearest 1°C) ____ °C

A — Answer

1. $-16 + 20 - 4 =$
2. $(80 \times 5) - (80 - 5) =$
3. $2000 = 2 \times 10^x$ so $x =$
4. $4\frac{4}{5} < \frac{49}{10}$ True or false?
5. $\frac{3}{10} + \frac{4}{5} =$
6. $1.2 \times 0.12 =$
7. $5.5 - \frac{6.25}{1.25} =$
8. Approximate 3.008 to 2 decimal places.
9. Evaluate 0.1^2.
10. If $a = 4$, $b = 8$, evaluate $\frac{a}{a+b}$ as a fraction in its simplest form.
11. $5x + 5 = 5$ so $x =$
12. Write down the largest number which is a factor of both 32 and 40.

B — Answer

1. If five carrots cost 45p, what will 40 cost? £
2. What is the interest at $8\frac{1}{2}$% on £1600? £
3. 1760yd = 1 mile. 2 miles = ☐ yd — yd
4. $\frac{1}{4}$ mile = — yd
5. In which millennium is the year 2010? — millennium
6. How far does an aeroplane flying at 720km/h travel in 5 minutes? — km
7. 20 muffins were bought for £10.60 and sold for £12.40. What was the profit on each muffin? — p
8. A square was enlarged by the scale factor 2. The new square has sides of 12cm. Find the area of the original square. — cm^2
9. 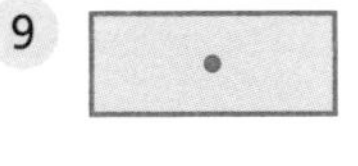 What is the order of rotational symmetry of a rectangle about its centre?
10. Eight bottles each have a capacity of 972ml. Find their total capacity to the nearest litre. — l

C — Answer

Jenny sets off from Leeds to travel to Nottingham. Lauren is travelling from Nottingham to Leeds. They arrange to meet at the motorway service station.

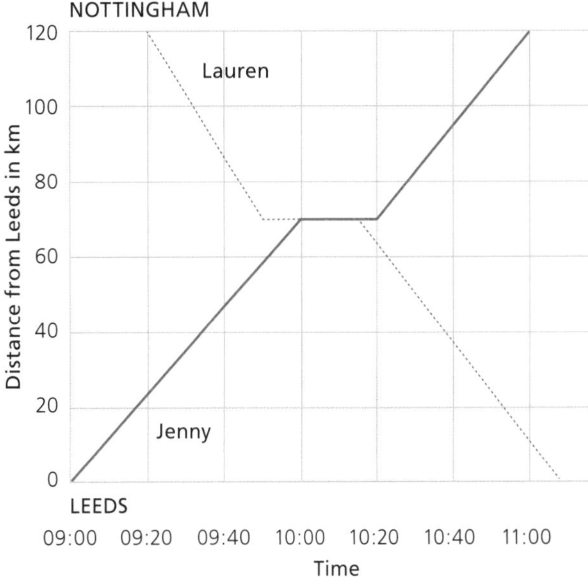

1. At what time does Jenny set off from Leeds?
2. At what time does Jenny arrive at the service station?
3. How long does Jenny take to reach the service station? — h
4. What is the distance in kilometres from Leeds to the service station? — km
5. What is Jenny's mean (average) speed in km/h between Leeds and the service station? — km/h
6. At what time does Lauren leave Nottingham?
7. How long does Lauren take to reach the service station? — h
8. What is Lauren's mean (average) speed in km/h between Nottingham and the service station? — km/h
9. How long does Jenny stay at the service station? — min
10. How long does Lauren have to see Jenny while they are both at the service station? — min
11. When Jenny reaches Nottingham how far does Lauren have to travel to Leeds? — km
12. What is Jenny's mean (average) speed in km/h for the whole journey from Leeds to Nottingham? — km/h

A — Answer

1. $-17 + 25 =$
2. $(80 \times 5) \div (80 \div 5) =$
3. Add 2×10^3 and 3×10^2.
4. Change $2\frac{4}{5}$ to a percentage. %
5. Add $\frac{3}{8}$ of 40 to $\frac{4}{5}$ of 80.
6. $5 \div 0.1 =$
7. $(3.5 - 3.3) \times (2.3 + 3.5) =$
8. Approximate 4.006 to 1 decimal place.
9. Give the answer to $2 \div 7$ correct to two decimal places.
10. If $p = 1$, $q = 2$, evaluate $\frac{pq}{p^2}$.
11. $2m + 4 = 10$ so $m =$
12. Write the next two terms of the sequence.
    1, 4, 9, 16, ___, ___

B — Answer

1. If eight sweets cost £1 then 36 will cost £
2. How much is a 35% deposit on a £480 laptop? £
3. $8\frac{1}{2}$ stones = lb
4. 3 gallons ÷ 6 = pints
5. Which three of the following were leap years?
   1410, 1600, 1704, 1900, 1992
6. How long does it take to travel 30km at 45km/h? mins
7. How many kilograms less than 1 tonne is 4 tonnes divided by 5? kg
8. A square was enlarged by the scale factor 2. The new square has sides of 10mm. Find the area in cm² of the original square. cm²
9. What is the number of axes of symmetry of this letter H?
10. Find the approximate number of days in five months. d

C — Answer

Below is part of the timetable of trains from York to Manchester. Note: *a* is arrive, *d* is depart.

York	*d*	06:25	09:13	11:15	19:48	21:48
Leeds	*d*	07:03	10:02	12:02	20:32	22:33
Bradford	*a*	07:23	10:22	12:22	20:52	22:53
Bradford	*d*	07:26	10:25	12:25	20:55	22:56
Halifax	*d*	07:37	10:36	12:36	21:07	23:08
Todmorden	*d*	08:00	10:59	12:59	21:29	23:30
Rochdale	*d*	08:14	11:14	13:14	21:45	23:46
Manchester	*a*	08:39	11:33	13:33	22:12	00:09

1. How many of the trains leave York in the morning?
2. How many of the trains arrive at Manchester between noon and midnight?
3. How long do trains wait in Bradford? min
4. At what time does the three minutes past seven train from Leeds depart from Todmorden?
5. At what time does the 9.48 p.m. train from York leave Halifax?
6. At what time does the five to nine train from Bradford depart from Rochdale?
7. What is the latest train from York that gets to Rochdale before 10.00 p.m.?
8. What is the latest train from Leeds that gets to Todmorden before 1.00 p.m.?
9. Which train from York travels the fastest to Leeds?
10. Between which two stations do trains travel for the shortest time?
    ___ to ___
11. How many minutes does it take for the last train from York to travel to Manchester? min
12. What is the shortest time in hours and minutes for the whole journey? h min

A — Answer

1 $45 \div 0.1 =$

2 $(80 + 5) \div (80 \div 5) =$ r

3 Add 1.4×10^3 and 4.1×10^2.

4 If the ratio of orange juice to water is 1:5 and there are 27.5cl of water, how much juice is there? cl

5 Find the difference between 10% of 20 and 20% of 10.

6 $1.99 + 0.19 - 0.91 =$

7 $\frac{3}{10} \times \frac{4}{5} =$

8 Approximate 0.003 325 to 3 decimal places.

9 Estimate to the nearest ten $\frac{555.3 + 444.8}{5.03 \times 3.99}$.

10 If $h = 2$, $k = 3$, evaluate $\frac{5h}{3k}$ as a mixed number.

11 $\frac{1}{a} = 2$ so $a =$

12 Write the next two terms of the sequence.
5, 4, 3, 2, 1, ▢, ▢

B — Answer

1 Find
a the cost of three sandwiches at £3.75 each and — a £
b the change from £20. — b £

2 How many pounds for €360 at 1.2 Euros to £1? £

3 33ft 6in = yd ft in

4 25yd ÷ 10 = yd ft in

5 How many hours in one week? h

6 What is my speed if I travel $\frac{1}{3}$ mile in 2min? mph

7 A right-angled triangle has sides of length 6cm, 8cm, 10cm. Find its area. cm^2

8 A rectangle with sides 4cm and 6cm was enlarged by the scale factor 3. Find the perimeter of the new rectangle. cm

9 H What is the smallest angle through which the letter H can be turned so that it again looks like H? °

10 Express 250 weeks to the nearest year. yr

C — Answer

Caitlin is checking the times of TV programmes.

BBC1		ITV1	
8.30 a.m.	Breakfast	8.25 a.m.	Disney Club
9.30 a.m.	Politics Show	10.15 a.m.	Story Keepers
10.15 a.m.	See Hear	10.45 a.m.	Morning Worship
10.45 a.m.	Deutsch Plus	11.45 a.m.	Mozambique Link
11.00 a.m.	Chinese Art	12.00 p.m.	Moving Abroad
12.00 p.m.	Countryfile	12.30 p.m.	Newsweek
12.25 p.m.	Weather	12.55 p.m.	Regional News
12.25 p.m.	National News	1.00 p.m.	National News
12.40 p.m.	On the Record	1.10 p.m.	Politics
1.30 p.m.	EastEnders	2.00 p.m.	Emmerdale
2.55 p.m.	Clothes Show	2.55 p.m.	Coronation Street
3.20 p.m.	Property Today	3.55 p.m.	Another Galaxy
4.00 p.m.	Football Match	5.35 p.m.	Simple Dinners
6.10 p.m.	National News	6.30 p.m.	Calendar
6.25 p.m.	Weather	6.45 p.m.	National News
6.30 p.m.	Regional News	6.55 p.m.	Weather
6.35 p.m.	My Choice	7.00 p.m.	Inspector Granger
6.40 p.m.	Baking School	7.30 p.m.	Coronation Street
7.15 p.m.	WW1 Investigated	8.00 p.m.	Matchmakers

1 How many minutes does Disney Club last? min

2 How many minutes of National News is there on BBC1? min

3 What is the total amount of Regional News on ITV1? min

4 How long is EastEnders on BBC1? h min

5 Which ITV1 programme begins at noon?

6 What time does the football match start in 24-hour clock time?

7 How long is the longest programme on ITV1? h min

8 Which programme is the longer, Simple Dinners or Property Today, and by how much? by min

Caitlin wants to record some programmes. She has 180 minutes of storage left and her television uses 24-hour clock times.

9 What time should she set the recording for the start of EastEnders?

10 How much space remains after recording EastEnders? h min

11 Is there enough space to record both EastEnders and Another Galaxy?

12 If Caitlin records the early showing of Coronation Street straight after recording EastEnders will there be enough space left to record the evening showing of Coronation Street as well?

A — Answer

1. $125 \div 0.1 =$
2. $(80 \div 5) - 80 =$
3. $500000 = 5 \times 10^x$. Find x.
4. Change 4:5 to twentieths.
5. The ratio of green apples to red apples is 9:5. If there are 45 green apples how many red apples are there?
6. $(0.125 \times 8) \times (0.25 \times 4) =$
7. $\frac{32.4}{5 \times 0.2} =$
8. Approximate 5.005 to the nearest tenth.
9. Write $10^3 \times 5.1$ to the nearest thousand.
10. If $a = 2$, $b = 3$, evaluate $a^2b + b^2a$.
11. $\frac{24}{x + 7} = 2$ so $x =$
12. $(1.5)^2 =$

B — Answer

1. Find the cost of 100 chocolates at eight for 50p. £
2. I buy 25 books at £1.40 each and sell the lot for £28. How much do I lose? £
3. 245in = yd ft in
4. $7\frac{1}{2}$lb ÷ 12 = oz
5. How many minutes between 07:44 and 11:18? min
6. How long will it take a rocket moving at 12km/s to travel 324000km? h min
7. How many ha in 5km^2? ha
8. A square with 3cm sides was enlarged by the scale factor x. The area of the new square is 144cm^2. What is the value of x?
9. What is the order of rotational symmetry of the letter H about its centre?
10. If 2000 identical boxes have a total mass of 1.88t find the mass of a box to the nearest kilogram. kg

C — Answer

Tom has four number cards.

4	6	9	1

Each card has a single digit on it. Help Tom to arrange his cards to answer the following questions.

1. What is the smallest three-digit number Tom can make?
2. What is the largest three-digit odd number Tom can make?
3. What is the smallest four-digit number Tom can make?
4. What is the largest four-digit even number Tom can make?
5. What is the smallest two-digit square number Tom can make?
6. What two-digit cubic number can Tom make?
7. Which cards can Tom use to show 13^2?
8. Which cards can Tom use to show 31^2?

Tom arranges his cards into two pairs. The digits on each pair form a square number.

9. Which two square numbers did Tom make?

Tom arranges his four cards to give the biggest number he can make and then rearranges them to give the smallest number.

10. What is the difference between these two numbers?

Tom takes two cards, adds the digits together, squares the result and writes down the answer. He finds he can then rearrange the two remaining cards to show this answer.

11. Which two digits did Tom add together?
12. What answer did Tom get when he squared the result?

A — Answer

1 $0.5 \div 0.1 =$ ______

2 $(80 \div 5) + (80 \times 5) =$ ______

3 Fill in the blanks.
$3^4 =$ ______ × ______ × ______ × ______ = ______

4 Write $\frac{5}{8}$ as a decimal correct to three places. ______

5 The ratio of grapes to plums is 12:36. If there are 36 grapes how many plums are there? ______

6 $0.1 \times 0.2 \times 0.3 =$ ______

7 $\left(\frac{12.8}{6.4}\right)^2 =$ ______

8 Approximate 1 470 000 to the nearest hundred thousand. ______

9 Write $10^4 \times 1.29$ to the nearest thousand. ______

10 If $x = 2$, $y = 3$, evaluate $x^3 - y$. ______

11 $2x - 12 = 0$ so $x =$ ______

12 $(0.6)^2 =$ ______

B — Answer

1 Share £3.60 in the ratio 1:2. £ ______ : £ ______

2 Which is the better buy

a 25 for 40p or b 60 for £1? ______

3 150lb = ______ st ______ lb

4 3 miles = ___ yd ______ yd

5 How many minutes between 21:53 and 02:42? ______ min

6 What is my speed if I travel $\frac{1}{4}$ mile in $\frac{1}{2}$ min? ______ mph

7 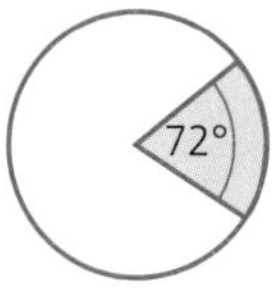

The area of the circle is $78.5m^2$. Find the area of the shaded sector. ______ m^2

8 A square with an area of $4cm^2$ is enlarged by the scale factor 3. What is the area of the new square? ______ cm^2

9 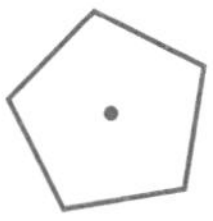
What is the order of rotational symmetry of a regular pentagon about its centre? ______

10 Five equal pieces of wood are cut from a plank 2.4m long. What is the length of each piece of wood to the nearest 10cm? ______ cm

C — Answer

Mum takes Leo and Paige out for lunch. The restaurant is serving a three-course meal. The menu is shown below.

> ***Menu***
>
> Starter
> *mushroom soup*
> *chicken wings*
>
> Main
> *Thai green curry*
> *chicken salad*
> *vegetable lasagne*
>
> Dessert
> *chocolate tart*
> *strawberry cheesecake*
> *ice-cream*

Leo orders his meal first.

1 In how many ways can Leo choose his starter? ______

2 In how many ways can Leo choose his main course? ______

3 How many different combinations of starter and main course can Leo choose from? ______ × ______ = ______

4 In how many ways can Leo choose his dessert? ______

5 How many different combinations of all three courses can Leo choose from? ______ × ______ × ______ = ______

Leo chose mushroom soup for his starter, chicken salad for his main course and ice-cream for dessert. When Paige orders her meal she decides to make a different choice on every course from that of her brother.

6 Write down the possible choice for Paige's meal.

Starter ______

Main ______

Dessert ______

7 In how many ways could Paige choose her starter course? ______

8 In how many ways could Paige choose her main course? ______

9 In how many ways could Paige choose her dessert course? ______

10 How many different combinations of all three courses could Paige choose from? ______ × ______ × ______ = ______

When Mum makes her choice she decides to differ from both her children but then discovers she cannot do this on every course.

11 On which course must she choose the same as either Leo or Paige? ______

12 In how many ways could Mum choose each of her other two courses? ______

Name:		Achievement Chart for Section 2 Tick the appropriate box for each question you got right.											
		1	2	3	4	5	6	7	8	9	10	11	12
Test 1	**Part A**												
	Part B												
	Part C												
Test 2	**Part A**												
	Part B												
	Part C												
Test 3	**Part A**												
	Part B												
	Part C												
Test 4	**Part A**												
	Part B												
	Part C												
Test 5	**Part A**												
	Part B												
	Part C												
Test 6	**Part A**												
	Part B												
	Part C												
Test 7	**Part A**												
	Part B												
	Part C												
Test 8	**Part A**												
	Part B												
	Part C												
Test 9	**Part A**												
	Part B												
	Part C												
Test 10	**Part A**												
	Part B												
	Part C												
Test 11	**Part A**												
	Part B												
	Part C												
Test 12	**Part A**												
	Part B												
	Part C												

REVISION TEST 2

1 What is half of 1.75?

2 $(72 - 48) \times \frac{72}{48} =$

3 $(3.25 \times 10^3) + (3.25 \times 10^2) =$

4 $56\% > \frac{5}{6}$. True or false?

5 Add $\frac{2}{3}$ of 30 to $\frac{3}{4}$ of 40.

6 $15 \div 0.1 =$

7 $54 \div (5.4 - 4.5) =$

8 Approximate 0.0789 to 2 decimal places.

9 Calculate $401 \div 5$ correct to the nearest ten.

10 If $a = 2$, $b = 3$, $c = 4$, $d = 5$, find the value of $\frac{bc}{a} + d$.

11 $\frac{1}{4}(x + 5) = 2$, so $x =$

12 What is the smallest number that is exactly divisible by 2, 3 and 5?

13 If six pens cost £2.20, then 15 pens cost

14 I put down a 30% deposit on a games console costing £420. How much is left to pay?

15 Change 2yd 1ft 5in to inches.

16 Reduce 10st by 10%. Give your answer in pounds (lb).

17 What date is the 100th day of a leap year?

18 How much cheaper is 300g of broccoli at 80p per $\frac{1}{2}$kg than the same mass at £1.10 per $\frac{1}{2}$kg?

19 A cylindrical tank is 1.2m tall and has a volume of $3m^3$. What is the area of the base of the tank?

20 A square with an area of $9cm^2$ is enlarged by the scale factor 4. What is the area of the new square?

21 What is the order of rotational symmetry of a rectangle about its centre?

22 16 bottles each have a capacity of 492ml. Find their total capacity to the nearest litre.

23 A point P has coordinates (5, 3). What are the coordinates of the reflection of P in the *y*-axis?

24 An architect draws a plan of a school to a scale of 1:500. If the school is 45m long what is its length on the plan?

25 Using the digits 2, 3, 5, 8 subtract the largest two-digit even number from the smallest three-digit even number. Each digit can be used only once in each number.

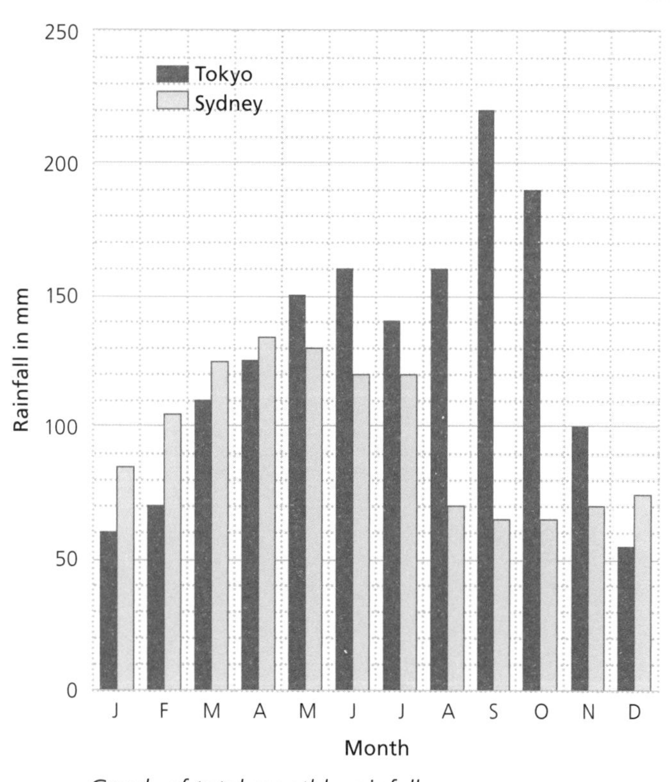

Graph of total monthly rainfall
for Tokyo, Japan and Sydney, Australia

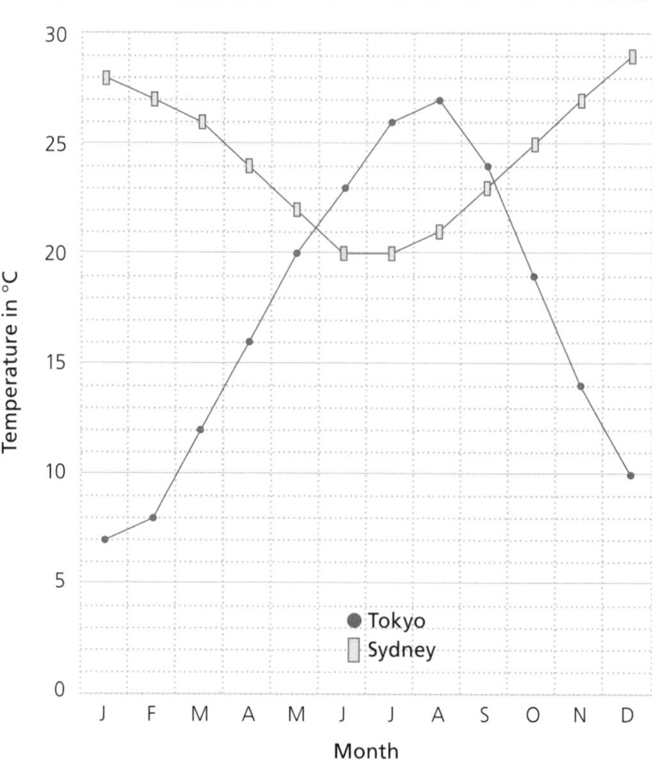

Graph of maximum monthly temperature
for Tokyo, Japan and Sydney, Australia

Look carefully at the graphs above and answer the following questions.

26 Which is the wettest month in Sydney?

27 Which month shows the greatest difference between the rainfall in Tokyo and the rainfall in Sydney?

28 In which month is the rainfall in Tokyo and Sydney most nearly the same?

29 How much rain falls in Tokyo during its driest month?

30 What is the range of rainfall in Sydney?

31 Which is the hottest month in Sydney?

32 Which is the coldest month in Tokyo?

33 Which month shows the greatest difference between the temperature in Tokyo and the temperature in Sydney?

34 In which month is the maximum temperature in Tokyo and Sydney most nearly the same?

35 What is the range of maximum temperature in Sydney?

36 What is the temperature in Tokyo during the wettest month?

37 Between which two months in Sydney is there no change in both rainfall and temperature?

38 What is the mean maximum temperature in Tokyo during its hottest four-month period?

39 What is the total rainfall in Sydney during its four hottest months?

40 What is the total rainfall in Tokyo during its three coldest months?

A — Answer

1 What is the remainder when 323 is divided by 7? ______ r ______

2 $(930 + 470) \div 14 =$ ______

3 Write in digits eighty-nine hundred. ______

4 Express $\frac{1}{8}$ as a decimal. ______

5 $3\frac{3}{4} \times 40 =$ ______

6 $2.8 - 0.07 =$ ______

7 $0.5 \times (2.5 + 7.2) =$ ______

8 Round 5.0827496 to the nearest thousandth. ______

9 Write 1286 correct to two significant figures. ______

10 If $a = 4$, $b = 5$ and $c = 6$, find the value of $a^2 + b^2 + c^2$. ______

11 $5u + 11 = 46$ so $u =$ ______

12 Write the next two terms of the sequence.
100, 10, 1, 0.1, ___ , ___ ______

B — Answer

1 I buy 16 slices of cheesecake at £2.75 each. How much change from £50? £ ______

2 The price of a £9800 car rises by 6%. What is the new cost? £ ______

3 2.54cm ≈ 1in. 75mm is approximately ______ in

4 40cm is approximately ___ in. ______ in

5 How many days inclusive from 15.10.2017 to 05.02.2018? ______ d

6 In metres, find the distance travelled in 2min at a rate of 16m/s. ______ m

7 Find the diameter of a circle whose circumference is 157mm.

$\pi = 3.14$ ______ mm

8 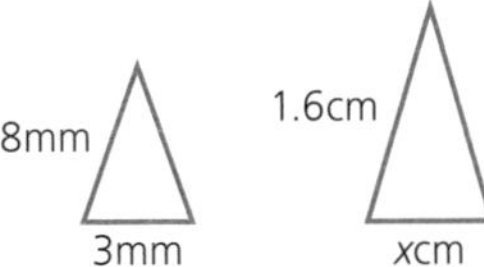

These are similar shapes (one is an enlargement of the other). Find x. ______ cm

9 What is the number of axes of symmetry of this shape? ______

10 Find the cost of six books at £4.95 each to the nearest £1. £ ______

C — Answer

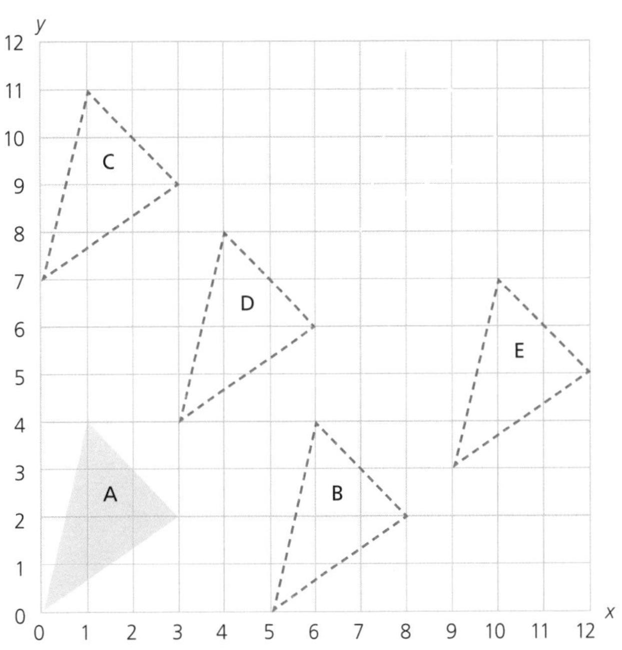

1 Write down the corner coordinates of triangle A.
(___ , ___) (___ , ___) (___ , ___)

2 Triangle A is translated to position B. Write down the corner coordinates of the triangle when in position B.
(___ , ___) (___ , ___) (___ , ___)

3 What happens to the x-values of the coordinates of the triangle when it is translated to position B? ______

4 What happens to the y-values of the coordinates of the triangle when it is translated to position B? ______

5 Use your answers to questions 3 and 4 to complete the statement: the mapping $(x, y) \rightarrow (x +$ ___ $, y)$ translates triangle A to position B.

6 Write down the corner coordinates of the triangle when translated to position C.
(___ , ___) (___ , ___) (___ , ___)

7 Use your answer to question 6 to complete the statement: the mapping $(x, y) \rightarrow (x, y +$ ___ $)$ translates triangle A to position C.

8 Write down the corner coordinates of the triangle when translated to position D.
(___ , ___) (___ , ___) (___ , ___)

9 Complete the statement: The mapping $(x, y) \rightarrow$ $(x +$ ___ $, y +$ ___ $)$ translates triangle A to position D.

10 Complete the statement: The mapping $(x, y) \rightarrow$ $(x +$ ___ $, y +$ ___ $)$ translates triangle A to position E.

11 Triangle A is translated by the mapping of $(x, y) \rightarrow (x + 7, y + 8)$. Write down the values of the corner coordinates when the triangle is translated by this mapping to its new position.
(___ , ___) (___ , ___) (___ , ___)

12 On the grid above sketch in the new position of the triangle.

A Answer

1 Write down the product of 142 and 9. ______

2 (72 + 56) ÷ (72 – 56) = ______

3 Write in digits nineteen hundred and eight. ______

4 Arrange in ascending order:

$\frac{3}{4}, \frac{2}{3}, \frac{4}{5}, \frac{5}{8}, \frac{1}{2}$

___ < ___ < ___ < ___ < ___

5 Divide 147 in the ratio 2:5. ______ : ______

6 0.705 + 0.09 + 1.03 = ______

7 0.4 × (4 – 0.08) = ______

8 Round 16.2534865 to the nearest ten thousandth. ______

9 Calculate correct to three decimal places. 2.43 ÷ 9 ______

10 If $x = 2$, $y = 3$, $z = 5$, find the value of $x^2 + y^2 + z^2$. ______

11 $3p^2 = 48$ so $p =$ ______

12 Express 42 as a product of three prime numbers. ___ × ___ × ___ = ___

B Answer

1 Share £115 in the ratio 3:2. £ ______ : £ ______

2 I buy a box of 48 oranges for £5 and sell them at 15p each. What is my profit? £ ______

3 10cm is approximately ______ in

4 1ha = ______ m^2

5 Which of these years was in the 2nd millennium BCE?
2850 BCE, 1725 BCE, 986 BCE ______ BCE

6 How long will it take to travel 2000m at 120km/h? ______ min

7 Abdul runs 100m in 12.5s. What is his mean (average) speed in m/s? ______ m/s

8 At what angle do the diagonals of a kite cross each other? ______ °

9 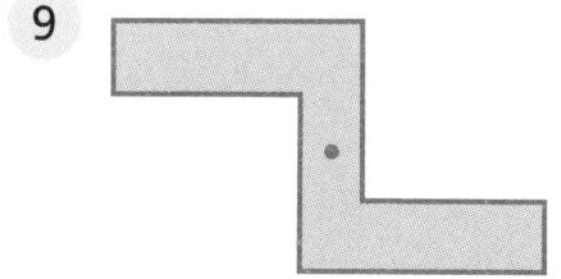
What is the order of rotational symmetry of this shape about its centre? ______

10 Approximate 3098mm to the nearest centimetre. ______ cm

C Answer

Daisy and Charlie play a game with spinners.

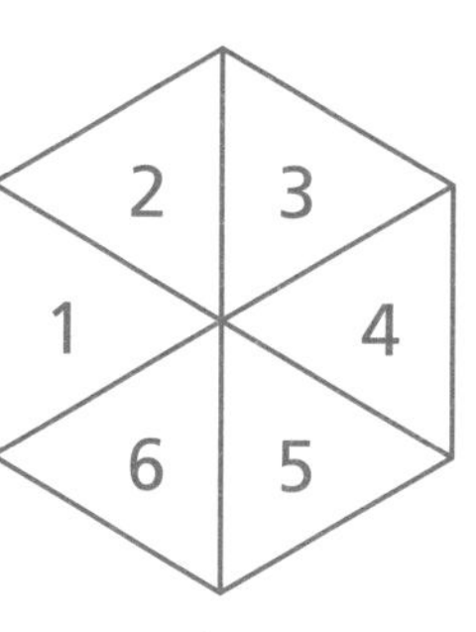

Daisy's Spinner

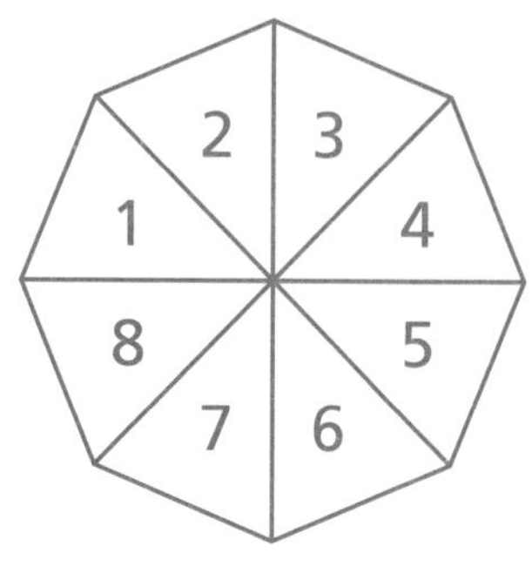

Charlie's Spinner

Express your answers as fractions in their lowest terms.

1 What is the probability of Daisy spinning a 6? ______

2 What is the probability of Charlie spinning a 6? ______

3 What is the probability of Daisy not spinning a 6? ______

4 What is the probability of Charlie not spinning a 6? ______

5 What is the probability of Daisy spinning an odd number? ______

6 What is the probability of Charlie not spinning an odd number? ______

7 What is the probability of Daisy spinning either a 5 or a 6? ______

8 What is the probability of Daisy spinning a number greater than 4? ______

9 What is the probability of Charlie spinning a number greater than 4? ______

10 What is the probability of Charlie spinning a number less than 4? ______

11 What is the probability of Charlie spinning either a number greater than 4 or a number less than 4? ______

12 Explain why the answer to question 11 is less than 1.

______

______

A — Answer

1. Write down the sum of 526 and 625.
2. ((15 + 45) ÷ 3) ÷ 2 =
3. Write in digits forty-six thousand and forty-six.
4. $33\% > \frac{1}{3}$ True or false?
5. Reduce 120 by $33\frac{1}{3}\%$.
6. 2.2 × 0.03 =
7. $\frac{8.4}{0.3 + 0.4}$ =
8. Round 0.00985 to the nearest thousandth.
9. Estimate to the nearest ten. $\frac{48.97 \times 52.6}{25.12}$
10. If $m = 4$, $n = 5$, $q = 6$, find the value of $m(q^2 - n^2)$.
11. $\sqrt{r} = 9$ so r =
12. Write down the prime factors of 20. × × =

B — Answer

1. If 45 envelopes cost £1.35 how much is this per envelope? p
2. Calculate the interest at 7.5% on a loan of £4000. £
3. 60cm is approximately ft
4. 32km is approximately miles
5. In a race Molly beat the previous school record of 23.17s by $\frac{31}{100}$s. What was Molly's new time? s
6. How long will it take to travel 42km at 18km/h? h min
7. A tank of volume 9m³ has a square base of side 1.5m. How tall is the tank? m
8. These are similar rectangles. Find x. cm

72mm

32mm

21.6cm

xcm

9. What is the number of axes of symmetry of this shape?
10. Approximate 355in to the nearest yard. yd

C — Answer

The table shows a spreadsheet that Ella used to investigate the angle properties of regular polygons. Two cells are empty. The diagram of a hexagon shows how Ella labelled the centre and interior angles.

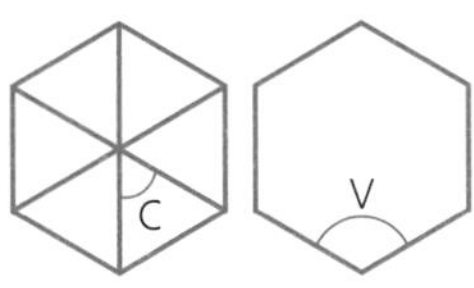

	A	B	C	D
1	Number of sides, N	Centre angle, C	Interior angle, V	Sum of interior angles
2	3	120	60	180
3	4	90	90	360
4	5	72		540
5	6		120	720
6	7	51.4	128.6	900
7	8	45	135	1080
8	9	40	140	1260
9	10	36	144	1440

1. Which row of the spreadsheet represents a hexagon?
2. What shape is represented by row 3 of the spreadsheet?
3. The formula used in the spreadsheet to calculate the angle at the centre of a hexagon was 360 ÷ A5. What value does this give for the centre angle?
4. Into which empty cell should this value be entered?
5. What formula was used to find the centre angle of a ten-sided decagon?
6. To find the interior angle of a pentagon the formula 180 – B4 was used. What value of angle does this give?
7. Into which empty cell should this value be entered?
8. What formula was used in the spreadsheet to find the interior angle of a seven-sided heptagon?
9. What value results from using the formula C9*A9?
10. Which cell contains this value?
11. What does this value represent?
12. What formula was used to find the sum of the interior angles of an octagon?

SECTION 3 | Test 4

A

Answer

1. Write down the difference between 308 and 803.
2. $45 \div ((3 \times 3) + (2 \times 3)) =$
3. Write in digits one million, thirty thousand and seven.
4. Arrange in descending order: 0.81, $\frac{8}{10}$, 1.08, 0.18 ___ > ___ > ___ > ___
5. Divide 192 in the ratio 3:5. ___ : ___
6. $4.8 \div 8 =$
7. $\frac{8.4}{0.3 \times 0.4} =$
8. Write 4703 correct to one significant figure.
9. $5 < \frac{14 \times 21}{42} < 10$ True or false?
10. If $a = 5$, $b = 3$, find the value of $b^3 - a^2$.
11. $\frac{1}{2}x^2 = 12.5$ so $x =$
12. Write the next two terms of the sequence. 1, $\frac{1}{2}$, $\frac{1}{4}$, $\frac{1}{8}$, ___, ___

B

Answer

1. If 500 marshmallows cost £12.50 how many marshmallows do I get for £1?
2. I exchange £220 into Euros at 1.3 Euros to £1. How many Euros do I get? € ___
3. 90cm is approximately ___ yd
4. 9.6km is approximately ___ miles
5. Change 18 minutes to midnight to 24-hour clock notation.
6. How far does a plane flying at 720km/h travel in 65min? ___ km
7. Two angles in an isosceles triangle are each double the size of the third angle. What is the size of the third angle? ___ °
8. These are similar shapes. Find the scale factor of enlargement.

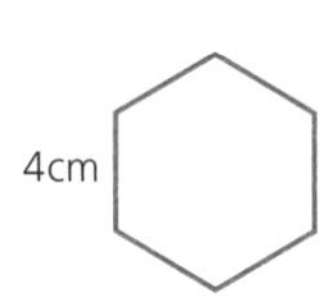

9. What is the order of rotational symmetry of this shape about its centre?
10. Five boxes have a mass of 2925g each. Find the total mass to the nearest kilogram. ___ kg

C

Answer

PrestoPrint – Online price list						
Printing	No. of pictures	Finish	Cost per print	Cost of prints	Extra set of prints	Total cost of order
6 × 4		Gloss	£0.11	£	£2.50	£
6 × 4		Matt	£0.14	£	£2.50	£
7 × 5	24	Gloss	£0.16	£3.84	£2.50	£
7 × 5		Matt	£0.19	£	£2.50	£
8.5 × 6		Gloss	£0.23	£	£2.50	£
8.5 × 6		Matt	£0.28	£	£2.50	£
					Total cost of printing	£

Ali has started adding his order to the form above.

1. How many pictures is Ali sending to PrestoPrint?
2. Does Ali want matt or gloss finish?
3. What size prints does Ali want?
4. How much will Ali pay for an extra set of prints? £
5. If Ali has two extra sets of prints what will be the total cost of his order? £

Evie wants 96 pictures printed. She wants 60 6 × 4 matt prints, 36 8.5 × 6 gloss prints and she does not want any extra prints. Fill in Evie's order on the form above.

6. What will it cost Evie for her 6 × 4 prints? £
7. What will it cost Evie for her 8.5 × 6 prints? £
8. What is the total cost of Evie's order? £

Jack wants 48 gloss prints at 6 × 4 and an extra set of these. He also wants 26 matt prints at 8.5 × 6 with no extra set and 36 matt prints at 7 × 5 with two extra sets. Fill in Jack's order on the form above.

9. What will it cost Jack for his 6 × 4 prints including his extra set? £
10. What will it cost Jack for his 7 × 5 prints including his extra sets? £
11. What is the total cost of Jack's order? £
12. What is the total cost of printing all the pictures? £

A — Answer

1. Write down the remainder when 85 is divided by 9. ______ r
2. $(45 \div (3 \times 3)) + (2 \times 3) =$ ______
3. $27 = 3^x$. Find x. ______
4. Divide 300 in the ratio 1:5. ______ : ______
5. Add 20% of 30 to 40% of 50. ______
6. $8 \div 0.25 =$ ______
7. $(0.5 \times 0.2) + (0.5 \div 0.2) =$ ______
8. Round 9.997
   a to 2 decimal places — a ______
   b to 2 significant figures. — b ______
9. $5 < \frac{3603}{61 \times 9} < 10$ True or false? ______
10. If $h = 2$, $k = 3$, find the value of $hk^2 + h^2k$. ______
11. $2k - 5 = k$ so $k =$ ______
12. List those numbers (except 1) that are factors of both 18 and 30. ______

B — Answer

1. I buy three ice-cream sundaes for £2.80 each. How much change do I get from £10? £ ______
2. A £150 bicycle is reduced by 12% in a sale. Find the new price. £ ______
3. 80in is approximately ______ m
4. 1g = ______ mg
5. How many minutes in one day? ______ min
6. How long will it take to travel 84km at 48km/h? ______ h ______ min
7. Find the area of a circle whose radius is 10mm. ______ mm^2

   $A = \pi r^2$ $\pi = 3.14$

8. 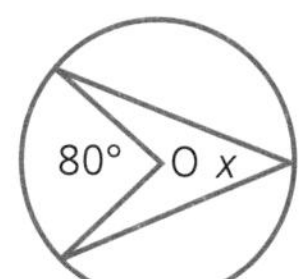

   If O is the centre of the circle, what size is angle x? ______ °
9. What is the number of axes of symmetry of this road sign? ______
10. Approximate 12lb 13oz to the nearest stone. ______ st

C — Answer

The diagram shows a plan of Mountjoy Park. The gridlines are spaced 1cm apart.

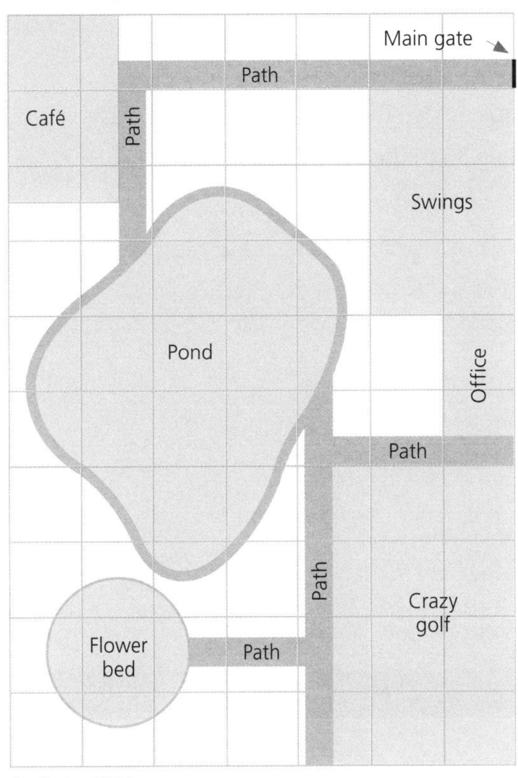

Scale 1 : 1000

1. What distance in metres is represented by 1cm on the plan? ______ m
2. Estimate the area used for the swings. ______ m^2
3. Estimate the area used for crazy golf. ______ m^2
4. Estimate the area of the office. ______ m^2
5. Estimate the area of the pond to the nearest $100m^2$. (Hint: count part squares equal to half or more as full squares and ignore squares less than half.) ______ m^2
6. If the pond has a mean depth of 60cm estimate the volume of water to the nearest $100m^3$. ______ m^3
7. Estimate to the nearest 10m the length of the path around the pond. ______ m
8. Estimate the diameter of the flower bed. ______ m
9. Estimate the area of the flower bed to the nearest $100m^2$. ______ m^2
10. Estimate the width of the straight paths. (Hint: look carefully at the paths near the café and the crazy golf.) ______ m
11. Estimate to the nearest 10m the total length of the straight paths. ______ m
12. Estimate to the nearest 10m the distance along paths by the shortest route from the main gate to the flower bed. ______ m

A

Answer

1 Multiply the sum of 36 and 25 by their difference.

2 $(45 \div (2 + 3)) \times (3 + 3) =$

3 $32 = 2^x$. Find x.

4 Divide 200 in the ratio 3:7. :

5 Divide 33 in the ratio 8:3. :

6 $0.7 - 7 =$

7 $\frac{6.5}{0.6 + 0.7} =$

8 Round 0.0909 to

a 3 decimal places a

b 1 decimal place. b

9 Estimate to the nearest thousand.

$\frac{(4.01 \times 10^3) \times (2.98 \times 10^3)}{1.99 \times 10^3}$

10 If $p = 4$, $r = 3$, find the value of $\frac{p^2 + 8}{2r}$.

11 $\frac{4}{n} = 2$ so $n =$

12 What is the largest number that is a factor of both 45 and 72?

B

Answer

1 I buy a season ticket for £80 and make 32 journeys. How much per journey? £

2 I pay for a £182 camera in 52 equal instalments. How much is each payment? £

3 2.2lb ≈ 1kg. $4\frac{1}{2}$lb is approximately kg

4 65kg × 20 = t kg

5 Write in 24-hour clock time seven minutes past midnight.

6 Change 1m/s to metres per hour. m/h

7 How many tiles 20cm square are needed to cover a floor measuring 4m × 3m?

8

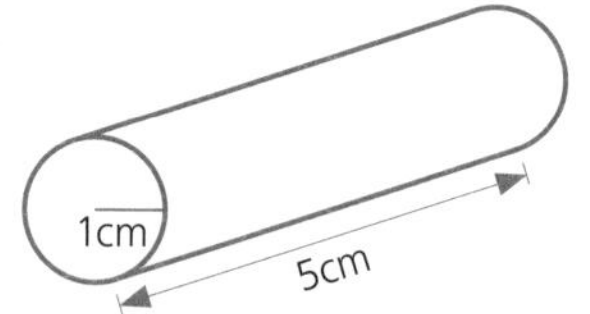

Find

a the area of the end of the cylinder a cm²

b its volume. b cm³

π = 3.14

9

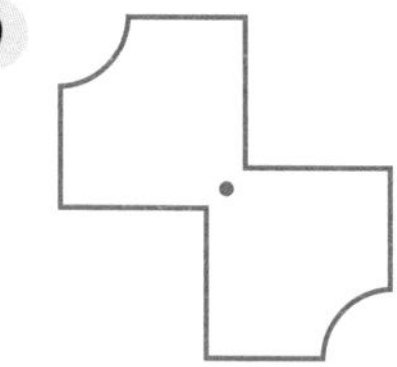

What is the number of axes of symmetry of this shape?

10 Find the area of a carpet measuring 290cm long and 88cm wide to the nearest m². m²

C

Answer

The map shows some of the main roads in Cumbria and the Lake District. The gridlines are spaced 1cm apart.

Scale 1 : 1 000 000

1 What distance in kilometres is represented by 1cm on the map? km

2 The distance from Gosforth to Carlisle in a straight line is 65km. How far apart are these two towns on the map? cm

Estimate to the nearest 10km the distances along the following routes. You may use a ruler to help you.

3 Carlisle to the seaside town of Maryport. km

4 Penrith to St. Bees via Cockermouth. km

5 Coniston to Carlisle by the shortest route. km

6 Kendal to Aspatria in a straight line. km

7 What area (in km²) is represented by 1cm² on the map? km²

8 What area is represented by the whole map? km²

9 By counting squares estimate what area of sea is shown by the map. km²

10 What percentage (to the nearest 10%) of the whole map shows sea? %

11 If the map above were redrawn to a scale of 1:100 000 would it be larger or smaller than the one shown?

12 If the map were redrawn to a scale of 1:50 000 what would be the straight line distance in centimetres from Gosforth to Carlisle on the map? cm

A — Answer

1 Write down the sum of the squares of 5 and 6. ______

2 $((2 + 3) \times 5) + 5 =$ ______

3 Write $2^2 \times 2^3$ as

a a number — a ______

b a power of two. — b ______

4 Divide 150 in the ratio 7:3. ______ : ______

5 $3 \div \frac{1}{4} =$ ______

6 $3.5 \times 0.3 =$ ______

7 $\frac{2.4 \times 1.8}{2.4 - 1.8} =$ ______

8 Round 478 711 to

a one significant figure — a ______

b three significant figures. — b ______

9 Estimate to the nearest hundred.
$\frac{(3 \times 10^3) \times (5 \times 10^3)}{10^4}$ ______

10 If $u = 4$, $v = 5$, $w = 6$, find the value of $3v^2 - (2u^2 + w^2)$. ______

11 $\frac{3}{p} - \frac{1}{2} = \frac{1}{4}$ so $p =$ ______

12 Write down the highest common factor of 30 and 48. ______

B — Answer

1 Share £495 in the ratio 4:5. £ ______ : £ ______

2 Games at £9.50 each are reduced by 10%. How much do I save if I buy three games? £ ______

3 4.5 litres ≈ 1 gallon. 95 litres is approximately ______ gal

4 18.4kg ÷ 8 = ______ kg ______ g
= ______ kg

5 At 8.25 a.m. an oven is set to switch on $5\frac{1}{2}$h later. At what time does it come on? ______ p.m.

6 Change 1m/s to kilometres per hour. ______ km/h

7 How many packets measuring 6cm × 8cm × 15cm can be fitted into a box measuring 24cm × 30cm × 60cm? ______

8 A parallelogram is drawn so that its smallest angle is half the size of its largest angle. What size is each angle? ______ ° ______ °

9 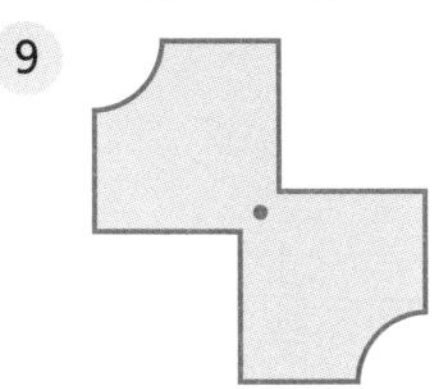
What is the order of rotational symmetry of this shape about its centre? ______

10 A shape with an area of $16cm^2$ is enlarged by a scale factor of 2. What is the area of the new shape? ______ cm^2

C — Answer

The pie chart shows the results of a survey in a large city into how people travel to work.

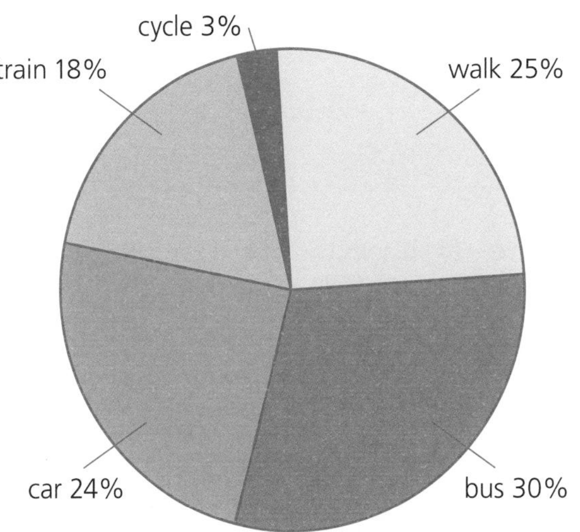

An office in the city has 513 employees. Use the pie chart to estimate the approximate number of office staff who travel to work by different means. (Hint: round the number of employees to the nearest 100 before you start.)

1 travel to work by bus ______

2 walk to work ______

3 go to work by train ______

4 cycle to work ______

5 do not use a car to go to work ______

A shopping centre in the city has 4897 employees. Round this figure to a suitable value to help you to estimate the approximate number of shopping centre staff who travel to work by different means.

6 go to work by bus ______

7 either walk or cycle to work ______

8 do not use a train to get to work ______

9 do not use a car to get to work ______

In this city about one million people go to work each day. Use this figure and the information in the pie chart to help you to answer the following questions.

10 A train holds about 500 people. Approximately how many trains will be needed for those who go to work by train? ______

11 About one-half of all the people who go to work by car are passengers. Approximately how many people who go to work each day by car are passengers? ______

12 About two-thirds of bus passengers are women. What is the approximate number of women who travel to work by bus? ______

A — Answer

1 Write down the difference between the squares of 6 and 7. ______

2 $\frac{35 \times 45}{5 \times 5} =$ ______

3 Write $2^2 \times 2^4$ as

a a power of two — a ______

b a number. — b ______

4 Complete the blanks to make these fractions equivalent. $\frac{3}{5} = \frac{\ }{10} = \frac{12}{\ } = \frac{60}{\ }$

5 $\frac{3}{10} + \frac{3}{5} =$ ______

6 $2 - 0.2 - 0.22 =$ ______

7 $\frac{1}{0.5} - 0.5 =$ ______

8 14.098 becomes 14.10 when rounded to how many decimal places? ______

9 $0.3 < \frac{3}{8} < 1.0$ True or false? ______

10 If $u = 4$, $v = 5$, $w = 6$, find the value of $3v^2 - (2u^2 - w^2)$. ______

11 $24 = 3(x + 5)$ so $x =$ ______

12 Write down the smallest multiple of both 6 and 9. ______

B — Answer

1 If 50 stamps cost £21.00 how much for 20 stamps? £ ______

2 Using the exchange rate £1 = €1.25, find how many Euros you would get for £604. € ______

3 1l is approximately ______ pints

4 80m ÷ 25 = ______ m = ______ m ______ cm

5 Karina works three shifts of $7\frac{1}{4}$h, $7\frac{1}{2}$h and $5\frac{1}{2}$h. How many hours altogether? ______ h ______ min

6 A car travels at 30mph. How long will it take to travel 5 miles? ______ min

7 A roll of tape is 25mm wide and 50m long. What is its area in m²? ______ m²

8 The acute angle of a rhombus is 40°. How big is the obtuse angle? ______ °

9  What is the number of axes of symmetry of this shape? ______

10 40 bottles each have a capacity of 248ml. Find the total capacity to the nearest litre. ______ l

C — Answer

Amy is investigating the area of rectangles. She calculates the areas by multiplying the length by the breadth and plots graphs of the results. Graph B represents rectangles of area 240cm².

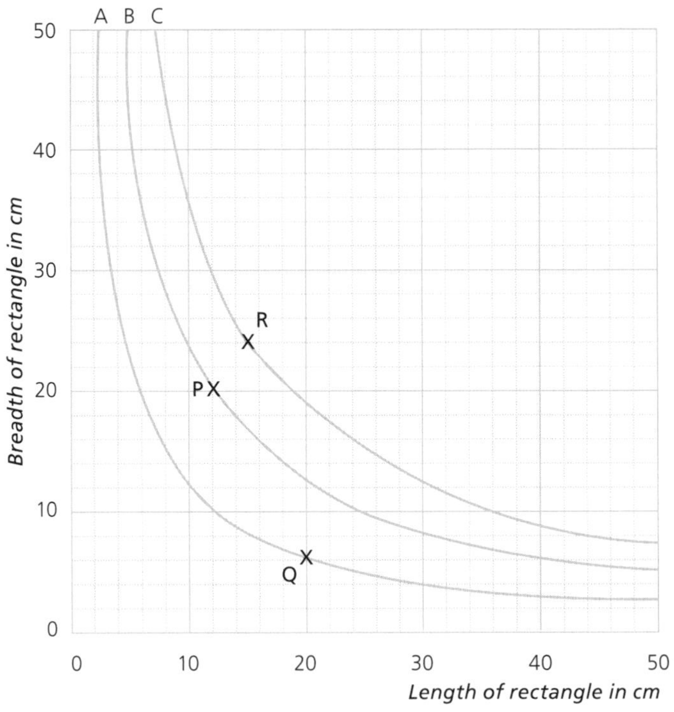

1 What length of rectangle is represented by point P? ______ cm

2 What breadth of rectangle is represented by point P? ______ cm

3 What area of rectangle is represented by point P? ______ cm²

4 What length of rectangle is represented by point Q? ______ cm

5 What breadth of rectangle is represented by point Q? ______ cm

6 What area of rectangle is represented by point Q? ______ cm²

7 What area of rectangle is represented by all points that lie on graph A? ______ cm²

8 Mark with an x the point on graph A that represents a square.

9 Use the graph to help you to estimate the length of the side of this square. ______ cm

10 What area of rectangle is represented by point R? ______ cm²

11 Mark with an o the point that represents a square of area 360cm².

12 Use the graph to help you to estimate the length of the sides of this square. ______ cm

A — Answer

1 Add the square of 2 to its cube.

2 $\frac{32 \times 72}{8 \times 12}$ =

3 Write $2^5 \div 2^2$ as

a a number — a

b a power of two. — b

4 Which two of the following are equal?
$\frac{3}{8}$, 3.8, 3:8, 38%, $3\frac{1}{8}$ — =

5 Write $\frac{7}{10} + \frac{4}{5}$ as a mixed number.

6 $11 \div 0.1$ =

7 $(1.5)^2 + 1.5$ =

8 130 940 becomes 131 000 when rounded to how many significant figures?

9 $6 < \sqrt{40} < 7$ True or false?

10 If $a = 2$, $b = 4$, $c = 3$, find the value of $5ab - c^3$.

11 $\frac{x^2}{x} = 4$ so x =

12 What is the lowest common multiple of 6 and 10?

B — Answer

1 If 240 pencils cost £15 how many pencils for £6?

2 I put down a 40% deposit on furniture costing £850. How much is left to pay? — £

3 28g ≈ 1oz. 120g is approximately — oz

4 6ft 6in is approximately — m

5 A coach departs 22:35 and arrives 06:15. How long does the journey take? — h min

6 A shape with an area of 4cm^2 is enlarged by a scale factor of x. The area of the new shape is 36cm^2. What is the value of x?

7 A bicycle wheel is 50cm diameter. How far does it travel in 100 rotations? — m

8 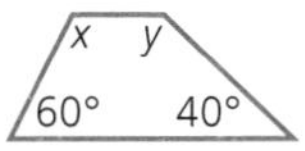

For the trapezium shown write down the size of angles x, y. — x = ° y = °

9 
What is the number of axes of symmetry of this shape?

10 Express 2h 25min to the nearest half hour. — h

C — Answer

Katy takes her car over to France and back. There are two ferries she can use from Portsmouth and two to return from St Malo. The table shows the ferry departure times and crossing times.

Cross-channel ferry Portsmouth – St Malo	
Departure times from Portsmouth to St Malo	7.30 a.m. 9.00 p.m.
Crossing time	8h 55min
Departure times from St Malo to Portsmouth	10.45 a.m. 9.25 p.m.
Crossing time	8h 41min

Katy departs on the early morning ferry from Portsmouth. It takes her 43min to disembark the ferry at St Malo and 85min to drive to the city of Rennes, 70km away. She then spends 1h 45min in Rennes and a further 1h 22min driving back to St Malo.

1 How long is the sea crossing to St Malo? — h min

2 At what time does the morning ferry from Portsmouth arrive in St Malo?

3 How long does it take to disembark the ferry and drive to Rennes? — h min

4 At what time does Katy arrive in Rennes?

5 How long does it take to travel from Portsmouth to Rennes? — h min

6 How long does it take Katy from reaching Rennes to arriving back in St Malo? — h min

7 At what time does Katy get back to St Malo from Rennes?

8 Is she in time to catch the evening ferry back to Portsmouth?

9 What is the departure time of the next ferry she can take to return to Portsmouth?

10 How long is the return sea crossing to Portsmouth? — h min

11 At what time does Katy arrive back at Portsmouth?

12 How long has the whole journey taken, from Portsmouth back to Portsmouth? — h min

SECTION 3 | Test 10

A — Answer

1. Add the square of 3 to its cube. ______
2. $\frac{24 \times 45}{9 \times 8}$ = ______
3. Write $2^5 \times 2^2$ as
   a. a power of two — a ______
   b. a number. — b ______
4. Express the ratio 35:63 as a fraction in simplest form. ______
5. $3\frac{3}{4} - 1\frac{7}{8}$ = ______
6. $0.1 \times 0.02 \times 0.003$ = ______
7. $(1^2 + 0.1^2) - 1.01$ = ______
8. Round 1 467 538 to
   a. 5 significant figures — a ______
   b. 2 significant figures. — b ______
9. $9 < \sqrt{90} < 10$ True or false? ______
10. If $x = 2$, $y = 3$, find the value of $(x + y)^2 - (x^2 + y^2)$. ______
11. $\frac{9}{m} = m$ so m = ______
12. $2^4 + 1$ is a prime number. True or false? ______

B — Answer

1. Find the cost of 360 envelopes if 45 cost £1. £ ______
2. I buy 12 pairs of shorts for £95 and sell them at £12.50 each. What is my profit? £ ______
3. 900g is approximately ______ lb
4. 2.5m is approximately ______ ft
5. Anwar leaves at 09:50 on a journey lasting $6\frac{1}{2}$h. When does he arrive? ______
6. A regular pentagon with sides measuring 42mm is enlarged by a scale factor of 1.5. What is the perimeter in centimetres of the new shape? ______ cm
7. $5m^3$ of concrete is used to lay a path 2m wide and 10cm thick. How long is the path? ______ m
8. To the nearest whole centimetre, give the circumference of a circle with radius 1.5cm. ______ cm
9. What is the order of rotational symmetry of this shape about its centre? ______
10. What is 588 seconds to the nearest minute? ______ min

C — Answer

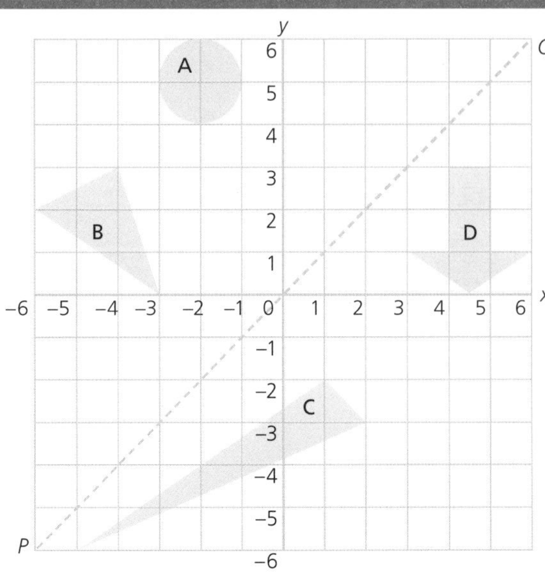

1. Write down the coordinates of the centre of circle A. (______ , ______)
2. Write down the coordinates of the centre of the reflection of circle A in the y-axis. (______ , ______)
3. Write down the coordinates of the centre of the reflection of circle A in the x-axis. (______ , ______)
4. Write down the coordinates of the corners of triangle B. (______ , ______) (______ , ______) (______ , ______)
5. On the grid above, sketch in the position of the reflection of triangle B in the x-axis.
6. Write down the coordinates of each corner of the reflection of triangle B in the x-axis. (______ , ______) (______ , ______) (______ , ______)
7. Write down the coordinates of the corners of triangle C. (______ , ______) (______ , ______) (______ , ______)
8. On the grid above, sketch in the reflection of triangle C in the y-axis.
9. Write down the coordinates of the corners of the reflection of triangle C in the y-axis. (______ , ______) (______ , ______) (______ , ______)
10. On the grid above, sketch in the reflection of object D about the diagonal line PQ.

Here are four statements describing changes that could occur when an object undergoes a reflection:

A The x-values of its coordinates stay unaltered and the y-values change sign (from +ve to −ve or from −ve to +ve).

B The y-values of its coordinates stay unaltered and the x-values change sign.

C Both the x-values and the y-values of its coordinates change sign.

D The x-values become the y-values and the y-values become the x-values.

11. Which statement A, B, C or D correctly describes a reflection in the x-axis? ______
12. Which statement A, B, C or D correctly describes a reflection in the y-axis? ______

A — Answer

1 $(3 \times 10^4) \times (2 \times 10^2) =$

2 $\frac{48 \times 66}{36} =$

3 Write $3^5 \times 3^3$ as a power of three.

4 Insert the symbol <, > or = to make a correct statement. 58% ____ $\frac{5}{8}$

5 $\frac{2}{3} + 2\frac{1}{2} =$

6 $0.3 \div 0.2 =$

7 $(1 + 0.1)^2 - 1.01 =$

8 2659 becomes 2700 when rounded to 2 significant figures. True or false?

9 $25 < \sqrt{250} < 50$ True or false?

10 If $a = 30$, $b = 40$, $c = 12$, find the value of $\frac{2a}{c} + \frac{3b}{a}$.

11 $w^2 + 4^2 = 5^2$ so $w =$

12 $(2 \times 3)^2 - (2^3 + 3^3) =$

B — Answer

1 I save £14.50 per month. How much have I saved in one year? £

2 I buy 495 American dollars for £330. How many dollars do I get for each £1? $

3 1600m is approximately ____ mile

4 1350mm × 5 = ____ m

5 How many years between the start of 1 BCE and the end of 1 CE? ____ yr

6 A right-angled triangle of sides 3cm, 4cm and 5cm is enlarged by a scale factor of 2.5. What is the area of the new triangle? ____ cm²

7 What is the speed if travelling $\frac{1}{2}$km in $\frac{1}{4}$min? ____ km/h

8 3cm, 4cm, x — Use Pythagoras' Theorem ($a^2 + b^2 = c^2$) to find the length of side x. ____ cm

9 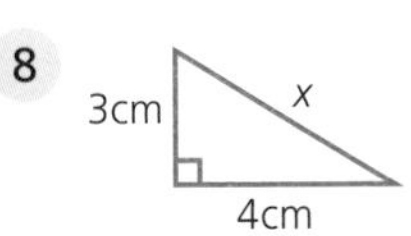

The word OXO is written diagonally across a square. How many axes of symmetry are there for the word and the square as a whole?

10 If 55 identical bottles can be filled from a 250l container, what is the approximate capacity of one bottle to the nearest half litre? ____ l

C — Answer

The children at Brightwell School are organising a lucky dip for the summer fair. Each prize has been carefully wrapped and placed in a large box. Visitors pay 20p a go and can choose one prize from the box. Since each prize is wrapped they will not know how lucky they have been until they unwrap their parcel. The table shows how many of each prize have been put into the box.

Prize	Number
chocolate bar	30
pencil	25
lollipop	50
sticker sheet	10
calculator	10
notebook	20
painting set	5
Total	150

Ryan is the first person to try the lucky dip.

1 How many lollipops are in the box when Ryan has his first try?

2 How many prizes are there in total when Ryan has his first try?

3 Express as a fraction in its lowest terms the probability of Ryan choosing a lollipop on his first try.

4 Express as a decimal the probability of Ryan choosing a chocolate bar on his first try.

5 Express as a decimal the probability of Ryan not choosing a chocolate bar on his first try.

6 What is the probability of Ryan choosing either a chocolate bar or a notebook on his first try? ____ in ____

7 If Ryan chooses a chocolate bar on his first try what is the probability of choosing a notebook on his second try? ____ in ____

8 If Ryan chooses a chocolate bar on his first try what is the probability of choosing another chocolate bar on his second try? ____ in ____

When Lucy tries the lucky dip exactly half of the prizes have gone but no one has won a painting set.

9 What is the probability of Lucy choosing a painting set on her first try?

10 How many tries would Lucy have to have to be certain of winning a painting set?

11 How much would this number of tries cost her? £

12 Is it possible that Lucy could win a painting set with fewer tries than this? Explain your answer.

SECTION 3 | Test 12

A

Answer

1. $(0.2)^3 =$
2. $\frac{54 \times 56}{63} =$
3. Write $3^5 \div 3^3$ as a power of three.
4. Insert the symbol <, > or = to make a correct statement. $1\frac{1}{8}$ ___ 1.8 ___ $1\frac{4}{5}$
5. $3\frac{1}{3} \times 10 =$
6. $4.8 \div 0.6 =$
7. $(0.2)^2 + (0.3)^2 + (0.2 + 0.3)^2 =$
8. 0.0387 becomes 0.00390 when rounded to three decimal places. True or false?
9. $6 < \frac{278}{39} < 8$ True or false?
10. If $x = 3$, $y = 5$, $z = 8$, find the value of $\frac{z}{1 + xy}$.
11. $50 = \frac{1}{2}a \times 5^2$ so $a =$
12. Write the next two terms of the sequence.
    $\frac{1}{2}, \frac{2}{3}, \frac{3}{4}, \frac{4}{5},$ ___ , ___

B

Answer

1. Which is the better buy
   a 40 for 50p or **b** 200 for £2.40?
2. A £395 computer is reduced by 8%. What is the amount saved? £
3. 5 miles is approximately ___ km
4. 13.53kg ÷ 6 = ___ g
5. Noah works five shifts each of 7h 50min. What is Noah's total working time? ___ h ___ min
6. Find the area of a circle whose radius is 2cm, to the nearest whole number. ___ cm^2
   $A = \pi r^2$ $\pi = 3.14$
7. Find my speed if travelling 0.25 miles in $\frac{1}{2}$min. ___ mph
8. A square with 15mm sides was enlarged by the scale factor x. The area of the new square is $144cm^2$. What is the value of x?
9. What is
   a the number of axes of symmetry and a
   b the order of rotational symmetry about the centre of the shape shown? b
10. If 720 equal lengths of electrical cable are cut from a reel of total length 500yd, what is the length of each cut piece of cable to the nearest foot? ___ ft

C

Answer

Javad has fourteen cards.

On six of them is a single-digit number.

3	6	5	1	0	2

On each of the other eight is a mathematical symbol.

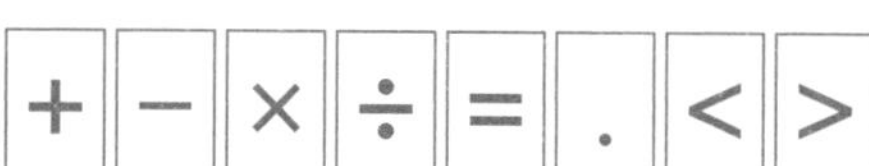

Fill in the blanks to show how Javad arranged his cards to answer the following questions. Not every card needs to be used but no card can be used twice in any one question.

1. [ ] × [ ] = 6
2. [ ] + [ ] − 2 = 6
3. 3 0 [ ] 6 = [ ]
4. [ ] [ ] ÷ [ ] = 1 2
5. 3 0 − 6 < [ ] 5
6. 3 6 ÷ 1 2 [ ] 0
7. 3 ÷ 2 = [ ] . [ ]
8. 5 = 6 ÷ [ ] . [ ]
9. 2 × [ ] ÷ [ ] + [ ] = 6
10. 2 6 = [ ] [ ] − [ ] + 1
11. 1 ÷ [ ] . [ ] = 2
12. 3 ÷ [ ] . [ ] = 1 5

Name:		Achievement Chart for Section 3 Tick the appropriate box for each question you got right.											
		1	2	3	4	5	6	7	8	9	10	11	12
Test 1	**Part A**												
	Part B												
	Part C												
Test 2	**Part A**												
	Part B												
	Part C												
Test 3	**Part A**												
	Part B												
	Part C												
Test 4	**Part A**												
	Part B												
	Part C												
Test 5	**Part A**												
	Part B												
	Part C												
Test 6	**Part A**												
	Part B												
	Part C												
Test 7	**Part A**												
	Part B												
	Part C												
Test 8	**Part A**												
	Part B												
	Part C												
Test 9	**Part A**												
	Part B												
	Part C												
Test 10	**Part A**												
	Part B												
	Part C												
Test 11	**Part A**												
	Part B												
	Part C												
Test 12	**Part A**												
	Part B												
	Part C												

REVISION TEST 3

1 Write down the remainder when the square of 8 is divided by 12.

2 $\frac{2}{3}(65 - 56) =$

3 What is the value of $2^7 \div 2^4$?

4 Share £550 in the ratio 5:6.

5 Write 24% of 35 as a decimal.

6 $325 \times 0.1 =$

7 $2 \times 0.2 \times 0.02 =$

8 0.00398 becomes 0.004 when rounded to three significant figures. True or false?

9 $\frac{1}{2} < \frac{27}{36} < \frac{5}{6}$. True or false?

10 If $a = 2$, $b = 3$, $c = 0$, find the value of $a^3 - \frac{bc}{a}$.

11 $\frac{27}{x^2} = x$, so $x =$

12 Write the next three terms of the sequence.
2, 3, 5, 7, 11, 13, 17, 19, ▢, ▢, ▢

13 If I buy 40l of petrol at 64.5p per litre, how much change will I get from £30?

14 The price of a car costing £12 450 rises by 4%. What is the new price of the car?

15 Which is the larger quantity, **a** 2 litres or **b** half a gallon?

16 Which is the longer length, **a** 2 metres or **b** 6 feet?

17 A TV programme begins at 11.35 p.m. and ends at a quarter to two in the morning. How long is the programme?

18 Freya runs 100m in 12s. What is her speed in kilometres per hour?

19 A delivery van has a load space measuring 1.8m wide, 2m high and 2.4m long. How many parcels each measuring 50cm × 60cm × 80cm can be fitted inside?

20 A parallelogram is drawn so that its smallest angle is one third the size of its largest angle. How big is the largest angle?

21 Which letters of the word TORCH have one and only one axis of symmetry?

22 Find the area of a garden measuring 11.85m long and 6.05m wide to the nearest square metre.

23 A point P has coordinates (–2, 5). It is translated by the mapping $(x, y) \rightarrow (x + 3, y + 3)$. What are the new coordinates of point P?

24 On a map of scale 1:50 000, two towns are 12cm apart. What is the actual distance between the two towns in kilometres?

25 12 coloured balls are placed in a bag. Three are red, four are blue and the remainder are green. If one ball is taken from the bag, what is the probability that it will be green?

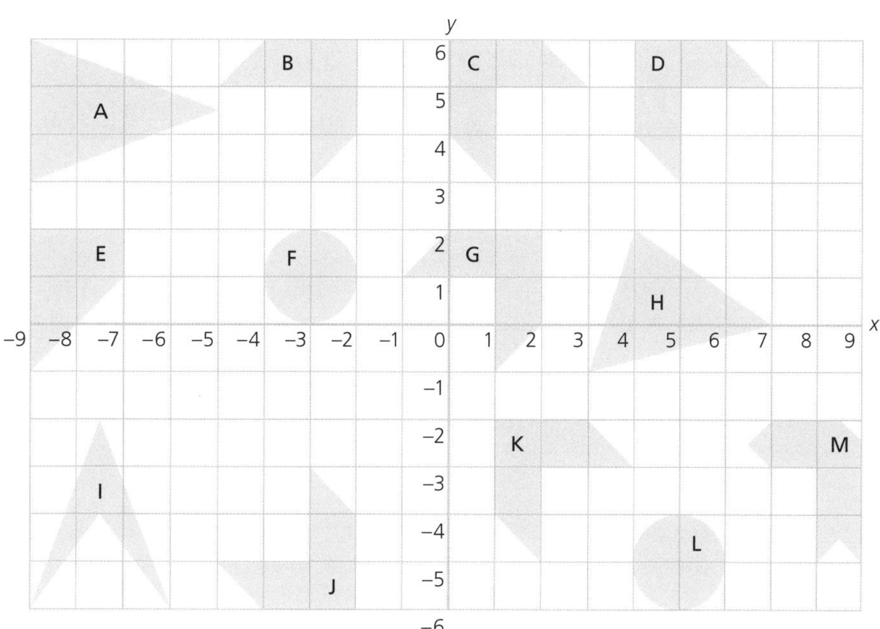

26 Write down the coordinates of each corner of triangle H.

27 Write down the coordinates of one corner of shape G that have a negative *x*-value.

28 Write down the coordinates of one corner of shape G that have a negative *y*-value.

29 Write down the coordinates of the mid-point of the shortest side of triangle A.

30 Write down the coordinates of one corner of shape I that have equal size *x*-value and *y*-value.

31 Which circle, F or L, has centre coordinates such that the sum of the *x*-value and the *y*-value is 0.

32 Which of the following, if any, is a reflection of shape B in the *y*-axis? Choose from: C, D, G, K, J or none.

33 Which of the following, if any, is a reflection of shape B in the *x*-axis? Choose from: C, D, G, K, J or none.

34 On the grid above, sketch in the reflection of shape M in the *x*-axis.

35 Which of the following, if any, is a translation of shape B? Choose from: C, D, G, K, J or none.

36 Write down the mapping that will translate shape K to position D.

37 Write down the mapping that will translate the centre of circle F to the origin.

38 Which shape has the larger area, K or M?

39 Which shape has exactly half the area of shape A?

40 Which of the following shapes have the same area as shape E? Choose from: B, D, F, H or M.

Schofield&Sims

the long-established educational publisher specialising in maths, English and science

Mental Arithmetic provides rich and varied practice to meet the requirements of the National Curriculum for primary mathematics. **Mental Arithmetic 6** extends beyond the Key Stage 2 curriculum, consolidating key subject areas alongside more advanced concepts such as profit and loss, using spreadsheets and conducting mathematical investigations. The accompanying answer book, **Mental Arithmetic 6 Answers,** contains Diagnostic Charts to support on-going assessment.

Mental Arithmetic comprises seven one-per-child pupil books with accompanying answer books, as well as a single Teacher's Guide. The series develops pupils' essential maths skills, preparing them for the Key Stage 2 national tests. It may also be used as preparation for the 11+, and with older students for consolidation and recovery. All the books can be used flexibly for individual, paired, group or whole-class maths practice, as well as for homework and one-to-one intervention.

Structured according to ability rather than age, the series allows children to work at their own pace, building confidence and fluency. Two **Entry Tests** are available in the **Mental Arithmetic Teacher's Guide** and on the Schofield & Sims website, enabling teachers, parents and tutors to select the appropriate book for each child.

Mental Arithmetic 6 contains:

- 36 one-page tests, each comprising the following three parts
  Part A: questions on number, calculation and algebra
  Part B: questions on money, measurement, geometry and approximations
  Part C: longer problem-solving questions
- **Achievement Charts** to encourage pupils to monitor their own learning
- **Revision Tests** to identify any gaps in understanding.

Mental Arithmetic Introductory Book	978 07217 0798 3
Mental Arithmetic 1	978 07217 0799 0
Mental Arithmetic 2	978 07217 0800 3
Mental Arithmetic 3	978 07217 0801 0
Mental Arithmetic 4	978 07217 0802 7
Mental Arithmetic 5	978 07217 0803 4
Mental Arithmetic 6	978 07217 0804 1
Mental Arithmetic Teacher's Guide	978 07217 1389 2
Mental Arithmetic Introductory Book Answers	978 07217 0853 9
Mental Arithmetic 1 Answers	978 07217 0805 8
Mental Arithmetic 2 Answers	978 07217 0806 5
Mental Arithmetic 3 Answers	978 07217 0807 2
Mental Arithmetic 4 Answers	978 07217 0808 9
Mental Arithmetic 5 Answers	978 07217 0809 6
Mental Arithmetic 6 Answers	978 07217 0810 2

First Mental Arithmetic is available for younger pupils

First edition published in 1998, compiled by E Spavin
British Library Cataloguing in Publication Data. A catalogue record for this book is available from the British Library.

Design by Ledgard Jepson Ltd. Front cover design by Peter Grundy. Printed in the UK by Page Bros (Norwich) Ltd.

For further information and to place your order visit www.schofieldandsims.co.uk or telephone 01484 607080

ISBN 978 07217 0804 1
Key Stage 2
Age range 7–11+ years
£3.50 (Retail price)